THE SPIRIT OF ENQUIRY

Caleb Hillier Parry, MD, FRS

BY

SHOLEM GLASER

ALAN SUTTON PUBLISHING LIMITED

First published in the United Kingdom in 1995 by
Alan Sutton Publishing Limited
Phoenix Mill · Far Thrupp · Stroud · Gloucestershire

British Library Cataloguing in Publication Data

A catalogue record for this book is available from the British Library.

ISBN 0 7509 0998 6

Typeset in 11/13 Palatino
Typesetting and origination by
Alan Sutton Publishing Limited
Printed in Great Britain by
Hartnolls, Bodmin, Cornwall.

Contents

List of Illustrations

Glossary

Cephalgia Headache
Dysuria Painful passage of urine
Ecchymosis Bleeding under the skin
Emprosthotonos Spasm causing flexing of the body
Epididymo-orchitis Inflammation of the testis
Glyster Enema
Globus Hystericus Imagining the presence of a lump in the throat
Hemicrania Unilateral headache
Opisthotonus Spasm causing arching of the body backwards
Orthopnoea Inability to breathe easily except when sitting up
Pia mater Vascular membrane closely attached to the brain
Polycythaemia Excess of red cells in blood
Radial The artery at the wrist where the pulse is usually felt
Scarlatina anginosa Scarlet fever
Thyrotoxicosis Abnormal increased activity of the thyroid gland
Variola Smallpox

Preface

Early in 1940 the Royal Army Medical Corps sent me to work in the military hospital in Bath. The Army had taken over the eastern half of the Royal United Hospital (RUH). Soon after my arrival the RUH senior surgeon, Mr Charles Kindersley, asked me to assist him with an operation for Parry's disease. Until then I had not heard of Dr Caleb Hillier Parry. My resolution to research his life and works has had to wait nearly fifty years. The work has been a fascinating voyage of discovery, in which I have received great help and encouragement from Miss Ann Parry, a direct descendant, to whom I am most grateful. Miss Parry has also allowed me to use family papers where relevant.

Most of what is known of the early history of the family was recorded by Dr Charles Henry Parry, Caleb Parry's eldest son. His findings are recorded in his article about his father in Macmichael's *Lives of British Physicians*, in his memoir in Britton's account of Bath Abbey, in his biography of his grandfather Reverend Joshua Parry and in his manuscript autobiography in the Bodleian Library. These have also been the main source of what is known about the family's life in Bath.

The main source of information about later generations is family notes, written by Dr Parry's great-grandson, Sir Sydney Parry, supplemented by Miss Ann Parry. Unfortunately only a few of Caleb Parry's own letters have been traced. His son Charles refers to the voluminous correspondence between his father and many well known people but this seems to have disappeared.

I am indebted to Mr W. Hamilton-Foyne for help with the history of the Grammar School at Cirencester, and to Mr David Roger for information about Warrington. Mrs Pat Strong in Edinburgh has provided copies of early documents of the history of the Royal Medical Society, Dr Batty-Shaw of Norwich has kindly sent me details of John Rigby, and Mrs Cobbold, Archivist at Ipswich, has provided details of Parry's marriage certificate.

Most of the research was done at the University of Bath Library and at the University of Bristol Medical Library, where the Parry Library is housed, and I thank most sincerely Mr Holbrook and Mr Ward for their help.

I am grateful also to many other people who have helped, to Mrs Richardson who typed the manuscript, and to my family for their encouragement and help.

I have used the following authorities for establishing priority claims for Dr Parry.

Garrison, F.H., *An introduction to the History of Medicine*, Philadelphia, 1924

Kelly, E.C., *Encyclopaedia of Medical Sources*, Williams & Wilkins, Baltimore, 1948

Morton-Garrison, *Medical Bibliography*, Cambridge, 1991

Schmidt, J.E., *Medical Discoveries. Who and When.* 1959

Singer, C. & Underwood, E.A., *A Short History of Medicine*, Oxford, 1962

Skinner, H.A., *The Origin of Medical Terms*, Baltimore, 1949

SG
Bath 1995

PART ONE

The Life and Work of Caleb Parry

CHAPTER 1

Birth to Bath, 1755–1779

Early Family History

Caleb Hillier Parry, whose father came from Wales, was born at Cirencester on 21 October 1755 and died in Bath on 9 March 1822, in his 67th year. Sir Thomas Lewis[1] says that the name Parry is derived from Ap Harry – the son of Harry. Caleb Parry's ancestors were long established landowners in West Wales. What is known about them is largely the result of a visit made by Caleb's son Charles Henry Parry. The original ancestral farmhouse was called Pendery and was in the parish of Llanfallteg near Narbeth in Pembrokeshire. Later the family fortunes increased and by 1760 they had moved to a larger house at Portclew, south east of Pembroke.

Charles Parry records in his manuscript autobiography that in 1801 he made a special journey to Portclew to re-establish contact with the main family, presided over at that time by John Parry, an old man. He stayed at Portclew for several days with John Parry, from whom he obtained most of his information. Charles was no doubt grateful to find that the family was highly respected. John Parry was Sheriff of the county in 1771, and in 1816 his son William held the same office. According to Charles this was the only known remaining branch of the family in Wales. The Welsh branch seems to have faded out in the mid-nineteenth century with William Edward Parry (1810–?). Sir Sydney Parry, writing early this century, thought that he might have emigrated to New Zealand.

The earliest record is of Richard Parry (1560–1641). His son, Thomas Parry of Pendery (1628–1720), had a very large family of twenty-one children. The estates passed to his eldest son Richard, and the John Parry, with whom Charles stayed must have been either a son or grandson. Thomas Parry's youngest son, also Thomas (1680–1720) was Caleb's grandfather. He died at the age of forty and was followed not long after by his wife. Their only child, Joshua, was cared for by his uncle David Parry.

Joshua Parry (1719–1776) was born at Llangan in Carmarthenshire. He was sent to school in Haverfordwest under the care of a Mr Davis and then, on an exhibition of £24 a year, to the Congregational Fund Academy in Moorfields. This institution, run by Mr Evans, was supported by Dissenters. Joshua, a talented pupil, studied for the ministry. While in Moorfields he became friendly with some of the members of Dr Samuel Johnson's circle, but not with the great man himself. Joshua had great literary gifts, and was an early contributor to the *Gentleman's Magazine*.

In 1741 he obtained his first post as acting Presbyterian minister at Midhurst, Sussex, and in 1742 he came to Cirencester as minister to the local chapel, where he followed Mr Evans, who had died that year,[2] and where he, in turn, officiated until his death.

On 9 June 1742 Philip Doddridge wrote to his wife

> We dined at Cirencester where I saw two or three wise agreeable people and a gay young spark, just come to be their minister, whom I cannot celebrate under either of the former characters.[3]

Cirencester, a town on the Fosse Way, was said to be second only to London in Roman times. Daniel Defoe[4] had visited it during his "Tour through the whole island of Great Britain", and he described it as a market town principally employed in the clothing trade. With its near neighbour Tetbury, Cirencester was the centre for the sale of wool from the north country. It was "populous and rich, full of clothiers, and driving a good trade in wool". "Wool" he writes, "is sold here in quantities so great that it almost exceeds belief". The trade of wool stapler was a profitable one and in 1784 there were fourteen listed.[5] Many fine merchants' houses remain as a monument to this lucrative trade. The present beautiful parish church, the church of St John the Baptist, is a good example of the old saying that most of England's major parish churches were built on the backs of sheep.[6]

It was in Cirencester that Joshua met his future wife Sarah Hillier whom he married in 1752. The Hillier family were long established in Cirencester.[7] From 1650 to the middle of the eighteenth century, parish records (births, marriages and deaths) show many Hilliers who carried on an extensive business in the town as wool staplers (ie buying wool and then grading it for re-sale).

Caleb Hillier (1686–1753), Sarah's father, was baptised on

23 October 1686 and was married on 27 April 1714 to Mary Brewer. According to the burial register they had four sons all of whom died young and two daughters, Sarah and Susannah, who survived.[8]

The Hilliers were strong supporters of the Presbyterian Chapel, and Caleb Hillier is described by Murch[9] as "a zealous and liberal benefactor of the Dissenters interest at Cirencester". He was one of the most successful members of the family, and, like the rest, was engaged in the wool trade. Gloucester Record Office has a letter from him to the Ashmead family concerning the weighing of wool. He also owned several hundred acres of valuable agricultural land in Gloucestershire – estates at Upcote/Upcott at Withington, and at Minety. (Minety is now in Wiltshire, as a result of a border adjustment in the nineteenth century.)

Joshua's chapel, the Old Presbyterian Chapel, was on the west side of the town in Dollar Street. The large estate on the edge of the town belonged to the Bathursts. The first Lord Bathurst, who was already friendly with Caleb Hillier, took a liking to and befriended young Joshua Parry soon after his arrival, and a friendship developed which lasted all their lives.

In later years, in his reminiscences, Caleb Parry recalled the night his father took him to dine with Lord Bathurst, shortly before the latter died (1775). He noted that Lord Bathurst had had a fall which reduced his activities. Dr Parry wrote that "tired of an existence . . . on such terms . . . he refused all sustenance", and died exactly a week later.[10]

Charles Henry Parry says of his grandfather;

> He was, during thirty years, the intimate friend and correspondent of Allen, Lord Bathurst, the Maecenas of the age; and was connected with Hawkesworth, Tucker, Doddridge, Lewis, Scott, and many other eminent men. He was an excellent classical, Welsh, and Hebrew scholar, and an admired contributor to various periodical publications. Hawkins, in his life of Johnson, informs us, that he was one of the original writers in the *Gentleman's Magazine*, and that "his head teemed with knowledge".

Joshua Parry and Sarah Hillier were married in 1752, and the next year (1753) Caleb Hillier died. Sarah, the older of the two sisters, inherited Broad Gates, the family home, and the valuable agricultural estates. According to Charles Parry, Joshua was left a tenement in Tewkesbury. The building was probably what would be described now as an apartment block. Susannah, the younger sister, married her cousin William Hillier in 1755, but died young and childless.

Joshua Parry

Joshua and Sarah lived for the remainder of their lives in Caleb Hillier's house, Broad Gates, in Gloucester Street. Later, when Joshua received several offers of preferment and invitations to move to London, he was happy to turn them down. He remained in Cirencester for thirty-four years until his death in 1776 at the age of fifty-seven. He was buried in the graveyard of his chapel in Dollar Street, and so too was his wife Sarah ten years later. In 1835 Jerom Murch wrote;

> There is neither a tomb nor an inscription, but the spot is indicated by a plain rough stone, which is well known to be the protector of Mr Parry's Grave.[11]

Joshua and Sarah had a large family, three sons and seven daughters, of whom only two sons and one daughter survived to adulthood. Sarah's first child, born on 21 October 1755, was a boy, and he was christened Caleb Hillier in memory of his maternal grandfather who had died two years earlier. The youngest daughter Amelia married Mr Benjamin Hobhouse (1793), later Sir Benjamin, who lived at Hartham near Corsham, and then at Cottles near Atworth (now Stonar School for Girls). Amelia was his second wife. Both wives bore him many children. Sir Benjamin had trained as a barrister, was an MP, and became President of the Bath and West Society in which capacity he and Caleb had common interests. He was also a banker with headquarters in Milsom Street. According to Meyler's Bath Guide (1823), when funds were being sought for the Bath City Infirmary (the old Pauper Charity), donations were accepted "at the bank of Sir Benjamin Hobhouse, Bart, and Co, Milsom Street". After Caleb's death he helped Charles Parry in his attempts to sort out the financial problems of the estate.

The present Hobhouse family live and farm at Monkton Farleigh. Sir Charles Hobhouse, the penultimate owner, said that his grandfather had Parry as a middle name, Sir Charles Parry Hobhouse (1825–1916). Sir Sydney Parry points out that this Sir Charles was not descended from Amelia, but from Sir Benjamin's first wife. Sir Benjamin Hobhouse became a Dissenter, while Caleb Parry and his wife, both from nonconformist families, joined the Church of England after settling in Bath.

The other surviving son, George Frederick Parry trained as a barrister. Charles remembered spending a few days in 1791 with uncle George in his chambers in Grays Inn, when his father took him to London. George Frederick was not very successful in his profession, and when the opportunity arose to emigrate to Guiana he was pleased to go. He died there in 1797, possibly from yellow fever. Years later Edward Archibald Parry, who became Bishop of Guiana, searched for his grave but was unable to find it.

Education – Cirencester Grammar School

Caleb was sent to the local grammar school in Cirencester; presumably, for there is no record, at the usual age of six or seven years. The school was a short walk from the Parry home in Gloucester Street and Caleb attended as a day boy. The school had been founded before the Reformation and was a typical grammar school concentrating on the teaching of the classics and a basic knowledge of arithmetic.[12] Later a rival school was founded in the town to cope with the demands of the merchants for a more modern education, one more suitable for their sons who would be going into commerce.

In 1754, the year before Caleb's birth, Cirencester and its school had attracted national attention. In the parliamentary election early that year, there were street riots between the Whig and Tory supporters, and one, Tom Jordan, was killed. "He was commemorated in a specially written ballad by Joshua Parry." Later that year the post of headmaster to the grammar school became vacant. "A dispute over the mastership . . . between Henry Wightwick and Francis James aroused much feeling."[13] The post of headmaster was a local appointment, and, as each candidate was supported by the rival political groups, there was a risk of local passions boiling over again. In view of these circumstances the authority to appoint a headmaster was removed from the local vestry and vested in the Lord Chancellor. The first headmaster appointed under the new system was William Matthews. He was followed by his stepson, Rev. John Washbourn, who was appointed in 1764. In some ways Washbourn was an unfortunate choice. The salary attached to the post is said to have been only £20 a year. Washbourn, not surprisingly, preferred to take paying boarders, rather than free local scholars.[14, 15] He was also a Fellow of Magdalen College, Oxford, with which he retained an active connection. By 1783 the school is said to have had only one pupil, and Washbourn returned to Oxford where he became Vice President of Magdalen. He retained his Mastership of the school until his death.

There are no details or records of Caleb during this period, but he was a bright intelligent boy, and probably did well at school. Jenner and Hickes had also attended the Grammar School, and the three are said to have started their lifelong friendship during this time.

Dr Charles Parry in his biography of his father[16] writes "Young Parry received the rudiments of his education at the school of the Rev. Mr Washbourn, at Cirencester, and there formed with the late Dr Jenner, a friendship which during the remainder of their lives contributed to the advantage and happiness of both."

In several books Caleb himself refers to his early friendship with Jenner. In a footnote in his book on Syncope Anginosa[17] Parry refers to the members of the Society which, for a few years, met at Rodborough.

> This little society, which met thrice annually during several years, at Rodborough in Glocestershire, and other places, for the united purposes of conviviality and improvement in medical science, consisted only of the following persons; Dr Hickes, of Bristol; Dr Jenner, of Cheltenham; Dr Ludlow, of Corsham; Mr Paytherus, of Norfolk-street, London; and the author of these pages. We were all virtually either school-fellows or fellow-students. The two last are to me comparatively of late acquaintance – of about twenty years: but they have been endeared to me by private and professional merits, and by habits of reciprocal obligation. Of the two first it is sufficient to say that they have been my friends for almost twice that period, acquired in the gay morning of my life, and faithfully preserved during various changes of place and fortune. My heart glows, while I pay them the tribute of esteem, which is justly due to their worth and unabated affection.

In the dedication to Jenner of his book on Tetanus and Rabies (1814) Parry writes "I cannot better evince the gratification with which I contemplate our mutual friendship, uninterrupted during nearly fifty years . . ." He signs the dedication "My dear and oldest friend, yours affectionately".[18] Similarly, in the reminiscences which he dedicated to one of his daughters some time between his stroke in 1816 (aged sixty-one) and his death in 1822 (aged sixty-seven), he states "Dr Jenner and I were at school together at Cirencester nearly fifty-six years ago".[19]

The 18th century was an exciting time during which there was an explosion of interest in and knowledge of natural history. The classification of plants and animals and the recognition that they belonged to identifiable groups grew considerably under the influence of Linnaeus. Parry, like most intelligent schoolboys, was probably fired in his imagination by gleanings from his schoolmasters of this expanding, exciting, knowledge. He is said to have collected bird nests, zoological specimens, pieces of different rocks, and the fossils which resembled the creatures he already knew. At Cirencester he could well have been encouraged by the older Jenner, and may even have made excursions with him. It is not known whether he had time or opportunity to continue his collecting when he was at the Academy in Warrington, or at the Medical School in Edinburgh, or in London with Dr Denman, but his interest was still alive and active when he came to Bath.

Warrington Academy

When he was 15 Caleb, ready for university, was sent to the Academy at Warrington. The entry "No 185 Caleb Hillier Parry of Cirencester, Age 15, admitted Sep 1770"[20] can be found in the Register of Admissions.

Oxford and Cambridge Universities were strict in their rules of admission and only took Church of England pupils, who had to accept and subscribe to the thirty-nine articles. Members of other denominations had to go to Scotland or the Continent to receive a university education. This unsatisfactory situation led a group of dissenters in the North West to found their own academy of further education at Warrington in 1757.[21, 22] It was designed to resemble the Oxbridge residential colleges, with the early buildings surrounding a quadrangle. The college attracted a wide range of talent in its tutors and was the nucleus of a wide intellectual circle in the neighbourhood, including Dr John Aikin DD and his daughter Letitia, who became the poetess Mrs Barbauld.[23] Later Warrington became the home of Unitarianism.

Caleb was an excellent student impressing teachers both with his character and his ability. A report from the college, quoted by his son Charles Henry Parry in the biography of his father,[24] gives a picture of the teenage college student.

> In a letter, addressed to his father, Mr Parry is thus favourably described by his tutor, the well known Dr Enfield: "He has such an uncommon share of manly sense, such a calmness of temper, and philosophical firmness of mind, that I think he may safely be trusted to the direction of his own mind. Indeed, my dear sir, you have great reason to think yourself happy in him. His genius, his application, his disposition, all promise great things. I hope neither your expectation, nor mine, concerning him, will be disappointed." His person is also thus described in a letter, written at the same period:– "He is more than ordinary tall for his years, and admirably well proportioned. In his air and deportment there is a gravity that, though he is not yet sixteen, he might very well pass for twenty. He is very fair, has regular features, and eyes the most penetrating, with an expression of great sweetness.

At the time Caleb was studying at Warrington, John Rigby was "provider of commons" to the Academy. The Rigby family came from

The Old Grammar School, Cirencester

Warrington Academy

Lancashire. John Rigby (1720–1793) had settled in Warrington where he married Sarah Taylor, daughter of Rev. Dr John Taylor of Norwich (1694–1761), a well known scholar and Hebraist. John Rigby not only supplied food to the Academy but also ran a hostel for students "When the Academy removed into its new house in 1762 commons and furniture were provided by Mr and Mrs John Rigby at £15 per session, etc".[25] Caleb, as a presentable young man lodging in the hostel, was probably included in the Academy's social activities and in this way must have met the Rigby girls. The attractive Sally Rigby was six years older than the tall, good-looking Caleb, but in spite of the age difference they fell in love.

Sarah (Sally), and her sister Elizabeth (Eliza) were friendly with Miss Anna Letitia Aikin, later Mrs Barbauld (1743–1825). In a letter to Miss Belsham dated January 1771, she writes "We have a knot of lasses just after your own heart – as merry, blithe, and gay as you would wish them, and very smart and clever: two of them are the Misses Rigby."[26] Sarah had devotedly looked after her invalid mother who died in 1773. This inspired Mrs Barbauld's ode "on her attendance upon her mother at Buxton", from which Sir Sydney quotes a few sentences – "Where blooming beauty in the noon of power watches and weeps beside a parent's bed". However in spite of this sad experience the Rigby girls seem to have been irrepressibly cheerful, and the historian of Warrington Academy records that these lively and attractive young women so distracted the students that they had to be banished from the town for a time. McLachland writes "Alas for the irresistible Rigby girls! Their winsomeness and their frolics became widely known to parents and guardians of the young men, and the Academy Authorities had even to insist on their banishment from home for a season in the interests of the students".[27]

John Rigby's eldest son, Edward (1747–1821), eight years older than Caleb, had also attended the Academy. At the age of fifteen in 1762, years before Caleb came to Warrington, he was sent to Norwich to be apprenticed to a local practitioner, David Martineau, a relative of his mother.[28] Edward Rigby had a most successful career at Norwich where he was attached to the hospital and became successively Assistant Surgeon, Surgeon and finally Physician to the hospital.[29] Elizabeth, the youngest Rigby (1752–1836) married Mr Joseph Bunny of Newbury.

Although Edward Rigby was eight years older than Caleb, the two men later became close friends. Edward Rigby certainly visited Bath and in Caleb's book on the Arterial Pulse (1816) he records that Edward Rigby was present at one of the experiments. The year before, 1815, Edward Rigby published *Observation on the Culture of the Mangel Wurzel* which he dedicated to Parry.

> Allow me to inscribe the few following pages to you . . .
> Your faithful Friend and affectionate Brother in law, Edward Rigby
> Norwich, August 15, 1815.

Edinburgh and London

Caleb left Warrington in 1773 and went to Edinburgh to study medicine. At that time Edinburgh had the most advanced and modern medical school in Britain. The dominant personality was William Cullen, who had transferred to Edinburgh from Glasgow where he had been Regius Professor of Medicine. Cullen became Professor of Medicine (1773) at Edinburgh. Apart from his large text book, he was responsible for two great innovations; he was one of the earliest teachers of clinical medicine using living patients, and he was the first in Britain to lecture in English rather than Latin.

In 1775 Caleb left Edinburgh temporarily and went to London for a period of study. Why he went to London is not clear. He lived as a house pupil with Dr Thomas Denman who had connections with Dr Aikin.

Thomas Denman MD (1733–1815), after an early career as a naval medical officer, and an unsuccessful attempt to establish himself at Winchester, came to London. In 1769 he was elected as physician – accoucheur to the Middlesex Hospital.[30] Caleb lived with Denman in London for two years. During this period he attended lectures and demonstrations by, among others, William and John Hunter. In his reminiscences he recalls them:–

> 'Dr William Hunter,' he says, 'was an elegant lecturer, and made his lectures very entertaining with the number of anecdotes which he introduced. But I remember once when he was showing round a corroded preparation, which was as beautiful as art could make it, it was accidentally thrown down. Nothing was said about it till it got to the Doctor; but when he saw it, it is not possible to express the horror he felt. After having scolded and sworn, he said, "I only wish that whoever did it, would take his money and go about his business. Let me never see or hear that such a monster exists." His brother, John Hunter, was of a somewhat different temper, or at least had the art of hiding his feelings. One day I was walking in one of the wards of St. George's Hospital, when a man was brought in who had fallen down on his head. There were fifty or sixty pupils present. He began lecturing upon the case. "What is the use," said he, "of the mischief happening, when one cannot see why it should happen and does not know why it happened? Now, if I had made man, I would have made him better." I heard him say this myself,' Parry

adds, 'or I should have been very averse to give belief to it. Neither had he the merit of originality, for the same thing was said long before him.'

His father, Joshua, died in 1777 and it is likely that Caleb came to Cirencester at that time. However, there does not appear to have been any major interruption of his studies due to his father's death.

In spite of the age difference Parry and Denman became good friends, and Denman recognised young Parry's true worth. When he was struggling to establish himself in Bath, Caleb wrote to Denman and in his reply Denman offered consolation and help. In 1785 a third edition of Denman's *Essay on the Puerperal Fever* was published, dedicated to Doctor C.H. Parry, Physician at Bath, "Dear Sir, The two former impressions of this Essay were dedicated to Dr William Hunter. . . . I am happy in giving you this token of my affection and esteem . . .".[32] It was a remarkable change from William Hunter to an as yet unknown thirty-year-old doctor in a small country town!

Jenner had also attended Dr Denman's lectures and obtained a certificate of attendance. This was in 1772 when Parry was still at Warrington.

Royal Medical Society

In 1777 Caleb returned to Edinburgh at a time of great and exciting changes in student life. A student society had been formally constituted in 1737 with 10 members, and at first they met in a tavern near the University.[33] They met to discuss whatever each had learned or read since the previous meeting. Later their meetings moved to a small room in the enlarged Infirmary, where they started a library with the funds previously used to pay for hiring the room in the tavern. By 1770 with the growth of student members it was clear that the accommodation at the Royal Infirmary was inadequate for the Society, and for its "library consisting of about 1500 volumes judicially selected from the vast chaos of medical literature".[34] In 1771 a committee was appointed to raise funds and as soon as a reasonable subscription list was reached (£210), the Society started to build its own hall on a piece of ground near the Surgeons Hall. The foundation stone was laid in 1775 by Dr Cullen, and the hall was opened in 1776. However it was realised that the legal position of the Society, ie the security of tenure of the property, was uncertain and precarious.

In 1777 a long petition, explaining the history and function of the Society and the importance of the library, was presented to the Town

Hall of the Royal Medical Society, Edinburgh

Council with a request for a charter of incorporation. The Provost referred the application to the Senatus Academicus for their opinion and this is recorded in full in their minutes.[35] In April 1778 at a meeting of the Medical Society with Mr Parry in the chair[36] the situation was reported and it was decided to pursue the claim. Caleb was appointed President during that year. It appears to have been the practice to have four presidents each year. He gave his presidential address on Friday, 1 May 1778 and it was one of only three to be published.[37] Caleb's address is remarkable for its mature and balanced sentiments and elegant construction. It is not on a medical subject, but deals with the problems of the Society and its properties. It ends with a rhetorical appeal to the members to be worthy of the Society. In June 1778 Messrs Parry and Athill were appointed to write to Principal Robertson. In June 1778 Mr Parry reported[38] that he had received a letter from Principal Robertson saying that the matter would be laid before a committee of Professors. Later in June at another meeting[39] it was reported that no answer had been received to the letter from the Society to Principal Robertson. It was, therefore, decided to seek legal advice. Counsel's opinion was sought and he advised that a Charter from the Crown would do as well as

AN

ADDRESS,

DELIVERED TO THE

MEDICAL SOCIETY

ON FRIDAY MAY 1. 1778.

After they had been for a Winter Session in the complete use of their Hall.

BY

CALEB PARRY,

ANNUAL PRESIDENT.

now Physician in Bath

first printed at Edinburgh in 1778.

EDINBURGH:

Printed by BALFOUR AND SMELLIE.

M,DCCLXXVIII.

Address delivered to the Medical Society, Edinburgh, 1778

TENTAMEN MEDICUM
INAUGURALE,
DE
RABIE CONTAGIOSA,
VULGO
CANINA.

QUOD,
ANNUENTE SUMMO NUMINE,
Ex Auctoritate Reverendi admodum Viri,
D. GULIELMI ROBERTSON, S.S.T.P.
ACADEMIÆ EDINBURGENÆ Praefecti;
NEC NON
Amplissimi SENATUS ACADEMICI consensu,
Et nobilissimae FACULTATIS MEDICÆ decreto,
PRO GRADU DOCTORATUS,
SUMMISQUE IN MEDICINA HONORIBUS AC PRIVILEGIIS
RITE ET LEGITIME CONSEQUENDIS;
Eruditorum examini subjicit
CALEBUS HILLIER PARRY,
ANGLO-BRITANNUS,
Societatis Medicae Edinensis Socius,
Et Praeses Annuus.

'Indagatio ipsa rerum tum maximarum, tum occultissimarum, habet
'oblectationem. Si vero aliquid occurret quod verisimile videatur,
'humanissima completur animus voluptate.'
CIC. QUAEST. ACAD. Lib. 4.

Ad diem 24. Junii, hora locoque solitis.

EDINBURGI:
Apud BALFOUR et SMELLIE,
Academiae Typographos.

M,DCC,LXXVIII.

Rabie Contagiosa 1778

incorporation by the Town Council. In August a petition was submitted, through the Secretary of State to King George III, requesting that the property be vested in the four presidents and their successors. It also asks for the Society to be granted a Royal Charter. The list of the four Presidents included Caleb Parry of Cirencester in the County of Gloucester now described as Doctor of Medicine. By this time Caleb had graduated MD. In January 1779 the Charter was sealed and the student society, became the Royal Medical Society of Edinburgh[40] – the only medical student society allowed to use to the title Royal.

Caleb Hillier Parry qualified MD in June 1778. His graduation thesis[41] on rabies, which was published, was in Latin and consisted of a review of the problems of rabies. It was dedicated to Lord Bathurst "Viro illustrissimo, nobilissimo, Henrico, comiti di Bathurst."

Marriage

Now that he was qualified, Caleb returned to marry Miss Sarah (Sally) Rigby. She was six years his senior, and outlived him by nine years.

The marriage took place at Palgrave, near Diss in Suffolk. It is not clear why the wedding did not take place at Warrington, Sarah's home, or at Cirencester, Caleb's home. Sarah had been friendly with Miss Anne Aikin, who had married Rev. Rochemont Barbauld. They had moved from Warrington to Palgrave where he had been appointed to the chapel (DNB). The friendship between the two young women seems the most plausible reason for choosing East Anglia, when both families were living on the western side of England, and at a time when cross-country travel was so difficult.

The entry in the marriage register states

> Caleb Hillier Parry of the Parish of Cirencester in the County of Gloucestershire and Sarah Rigby of this Parish single woman married in this Church by Licence on this 23rd day of September in the year one thousand seven hundred and seventy eight by me H Robinson Curate.
>
> This marriage was solemnized between us — Signed
C H Parry
S Rigby
>
> In the presence of Philip Meadows
Eliza Rigby
H Taylor
>
> Rochemont Barbauld
A Barbauld
Hen. Browne.[42]

"Sarah Rigby of this Parish" certainly suggests that she had left Warrington, her mother having died five years earlier, and had

Sarah Rigby

followed her friends, the Barbaulds, to Palgrave. There was no Parry among the witnesses.

Mrs Barbauld composed a hymn for the occasion,[43] which was included by James Martineau (1805–1900) in his hymnals, beginning

How blest the sacred tie that binds
In union sweet according minds!
How swift the heavenly course they run
Whose hearts, whose fate, whose hopes are one

With Sarah's "amiable disposition and engaging manners" she was to prove an exemplary wife and devoted mother. As in most medical households with the father's irregular hours, the mother was the hub around whom everything revolved, the person who created the family atmosphere and held all the members together. In his last years, when Caleb was paralysed by a stroke she looked after him with care and devotion.

After their marriage Caleb and Sarah made a long tour of Northern Europe, visiting Holland, Flanders, France, and possibly Hanover. But there is little detail of exactly where they went or what they did and saw. They must have been away for nearly nine months, and from the knowledge of Caleb's character and intense interest in his work it is difficult to believe that it was purely a holiday.

It is at least, probable that he spent some time at Leyden. During the latter part of the seventeenth and most of the eighteenth centuries there was a close link between Edinburgh and Leyden. The first Professor of Medicine in Edinburgh, Sir Robert Sibbald, appointed in 1685, had studied at Leyden. And in 1692 an Edinburgh graduate, Dr Archibald Pitcairne, became Professor of Medicine at Leyden, preceding the great Hermann Boerhaave who was one of his students.[44] They may have visited the University of Gottingen, which in 1801 made Caleb a member of its Society of Natural History. They visited Utrecht, and in his reminiscences Caleb recalled that they had attended a concert there. They also visited Paris.

They returned to the Parry home, Broadgates, in Cirencester in June 1779 to join his widowed mother, and it was there that their first son, Charles Henry, was born. In November they moved to Bath, to the recently built Catharine Place, and settled at No 13 where they stayed until 1800 when they moved to 27 Circus. The family increased steadily. Sarah bore nine children, four boys and five girls. One of the boys, George Rodney, died in infancy.

CHAPTER 2

13 Catharine Place, 1779–1799

The Medical Scene

In Parry's day, the majority of practitioners trained by a system of apprenticeships, and were usually called surgeons, or apothecaries, or surgeon-apothecaries. Such a one was Edward Jenner. A smaller group went to university where they studied the classical texts, but had little or no "hands on" experience of dealing with real patients. Finally after presenting a thesis, usually in Latin, they received a Doctor of Medicine degree, and were known as physicians. In some universities, Leyden and Edinburgh are good examples, they practised on live patients, but in others such as Oxford or Cambridge the MD was based largely on theoretical knowledge. There was no organised postgraduate training. However, many doctors spent a year or longer visiting clinics in Western Europe. Nearly all visited Leyden, which, under the powerful influence of Boerhaave, had replaced Padua as the medical Mecca. As already noted, this was the road that Parry took.

Bath in 1779 had not reached its zenith, but already it was a popular town for the wealthy, whether they were ill, or just seeking the pleasures of the gambling and the social activities of a fashionable spa. Jane Austen, who lived in Bath for several periods contemporary with Parry's later years, has left a vivid picture in her letters and novels of the social round in Bath. The eighteenth century was a period when the town was being converted from a crowded medieval slum into a planned Georgian town. The chief architect of this change was John Wood the elder, who was followed by his son and many other distinguished architects during Parry's lifetime who were constantly building and developing more areas of the surrounding land.

By 1779 much of the important development was complete and many of John Wood's plans and visions had been realised, Queen Square, with Gay Street leading to the Circus, and Brock Street connecting with the

Royal Crescent. Around this nucleus new terraces and squares were being built and the town was spreading far beyond the old medieval boundaries. The fame of the Hot Springs and their attraction as a seasonal diversion for the rich and the noble meant that a large number of the new buildings were designed for rental or as lodging houses. The medical demands of the influx of visitors led to a large number of doctors of all degrees of skill and qualification settling in Bath.

Building of the General Hospital in Upper Borough Walls was started in 1738, and its doors opened for patients in 1742. Its rules and regulations were such that it accepted only patients from outside Bath. No service was provided for the local community. However in 1747 a hospital was founded "for the reception of those diseased poor of the several parishes of St Peter and Paul, St James, St Michael, Walcot and Bathwick, whose means were insufficient to afford them the assistance of medical advice and chirurgical skill".[1] The Pauper Charity, as it was named, was located in the residence previously occupied by Dr Samuel Bave, in Lower Borough Walls.[2] This was the situation when Parry arrived.

Later, in 1788, Mr James Norman founded the Casualty Hospital in a house at No. 38 Kingsmead Square, to treat people injured in accidents. Caleb Parry acted as physician and his case records contain several accounts of people seen at this hospital.

Several changes occurred in the hospitals in Bath during 1792. Subscribers founded the Puerperal Child-Bed Charity for the relief of poor married women at home at the time of child bearing. Parry was the first physician, and the surgeon was James Norman. Parry had resigned from the Pauper Charity, which had grown steadily, and which in 1792 changed its name to the Bath City Infirmary and City Dispensary. The premises were enlarged by taking in the adjacent Alfred Hotel[3] and in 1823/4 the Infirmary joined with the Casualty Hospital to form the United Hospital.

In 1779, when Parry came to Bath, William Falconer was probably the leading physician. Henry Harington, another prominent physician, was still active but his main interest was music, and it is for this that he is remembered today.

Early Years

Dr Caleb Hillier Parry M.D. Edinburgh, twenty-four years old, arrived in Bath in November 1779, and settled in the recently built Catharine Place. No. 13 must have seemed very large for a young couple with only one child, but the family increased steadily until there were eight surviving children, by which time the house must have become very crowded. His son Charles, in his short biography of his father,[4] reports on his findings of his father's early earnings, and notes that in his first year Parry earned £39-19-0. Charles justifies the inclusion of these financial details thus "It may not be altogether without interest and benefit to the junior members of the profession, to lay before them the progressive increase which appears to have taken place in Dr Parry's pecuniary profits."

Parry was not fully occupied and was worried by the slow progress of his practice. He wrote to his old teacher and friend Dr Denman. Parry's letters have not survived but Denman's replies give a good idea of what Parry must have written. In December 1780 Denman wrote commending his decision to settle in Bath, but telling him "You must not be dispirited if the attempts you make often fail to answer your expectations. . . ." Nearly a year later, in October 1781 there was another letter from Denman, once again combining encouragement and consolation "I am not surprised that you find your receipts come in slowly at present, but all young practitioners think, when they set up their standard, that the world should immediately flock to it, and they are generally disturbed when they find the contrary. But all business is progressive, and the steps now taken may be so calculated as to produce their effect ten years hence. . . ."

Parry was unable to sit around idle. During his early days he had developed an interest in collecting fossils, and he filled some of his time with excursions to increase his collection. He rode over to Berkeley to visit Jenner, and spent the day specimen hunting. Jenner had made a large collection of fossils from the oolite and lias strata of the nearby rocks, and had sent many specimens to John Hunter ". . . and to his friend Dr Parry at Bath, who sometimes came to Pyrton to ransack the treasures which are found in the lias of that place . . ."

He wrote to Jenner in 1781.[5]

> My good Friend,
> I should have written to you before, had I not waited to announce to you the sending off of a small cargo of fossils and insects. But I have been altogether unable to procure anything, or any number of things, from the neighbourhood, of the former kind, which could at all deserve your notice. Of the latter, I shall send you about a hundred specimens, as soon as I can get them properly disposed in a box, so as to bear the carriage. Have you made any additions to any of your collections? I wish it was in my power to visit you and Pyrton at a season when I could take advantage of the dashing tides. However, I must learn to be content with such things as I have.

In this letter of 1781 Parry wrote to Jenner addressing him "My good friend". Young Parry had only been in Bath for two years. In those days of great formality in letter writing, when even wives and husbands often addressed each other as Mr or Mrs, such an informal and familiar mode of address implies a close and long standing friendship. For the rest of their lives they remained close friends and saw much of each other. Baron[6] writes "His acquaintance with Jenner commenced when they were at school together in Cirencester. Early intimacy and corresponding studies and tastes, laid the basis of a friendship which endured through every vicissitude of life. By means of letters, and as frequent personal intercourse as the nature of their occupations would permit, they stimulated each other in the pursuit of knowledge."

In 1855 the following short note appeared in the *Gloucestershire Notes and Queries* Vol. 4, p. 507.

> Dr Parry's proposed "History of Gloucestershire Fossils".
> Caleb Hillier Parry MD FRS, who was born at Cirencester in 1755, and died at Bath in 1822, published in 1781 "Proposals for the History of the Fossils of Gloucestershire", the introduction to which was intended to include all that was known on the subject of organic remains, and the result of many experiments and observations in which he had been long and ardently engaged. As his son has stated in the memoir in Lives of British Physicians, p.300 ("Murray's Family Library") his father's "increasing avocations suspended, and finally prevented, the completion of this work, but his remaining MSS are sufficient proof of his industry, knowledge, and discrimination". Where are these MSS at present? and are they likely at any time to appear in print?
> Signed Gloucestrensis
>
> (In Gloucestershire Collection, Gloucester Reference Library)

Neither the manuscripts nor the book can be traced. They are not known at the British Library nor at the Wellcome Institute.

However, the British Library has a broadsheet published by Parry on 21 August, 1782 appealing for specimens and stating that he is attempting to publish a *Systematic Arrangement of the fossils of Gloucestershire*. Probably this was the publication to which Charles was referring.

Parry needed to become known in Bath, and digging for geological specimens in the Severn valley was not going to help his progress. He did the obvious things. He joined the local societies, the Bath and West of England Society, and the short-lived Philosophical Society. He also obtained an appointment to the staff of the Pauper Charity. The Bath and West Society, still in existence, was the most important and most active society in Bath. Its membership included important landowners in the surrounding district, as well as a large number of clergy, doctors, lawyers etc. It produced two regular publications, *Rules, Orders and Premiums*, and *Bath Society Papers*. The *Rules* contained the lists of members and committees. Parry's entries on the membership lists show how slow it was for him to become recognised. The first entry in 1782 gives M.D. as his initials. In 1783 he had become Parry – M.D., and only in 1786 was he entered correctly as Parry, Caleb, M.D. This was the year of his first publication in the *Bath and West Papers* (See Rhubarb). Parry remained a member of the Society for the rest of his life. He served on several committees, and became one of the Vice-Presidents, an honorary title he shared with several other people. He was an active member, and contributed several papers to the journal. He took part in the annual shows and won many prizes. Later his close connection with the Society was enhanced by the marriage of his sister Amelia to Sir Benjamin Hobhouse, who served as President of the Society from 1805 to 1816.

Joining the Philosophical Society gave him the chance to meet and become friendly with some important scientists. The members included, among others, William Herschel and Joseph Priestley. This society only lasted eight years, 1779–1787.[7]

The Hydrogen Balloon

In 1783 the scientific world was fascinated with the demonstration by the Montgolfier brothers that it was possible to fly a heavier than air balloon using hot air. This was followed in December 1783 with a manned flight by J.A.C. Charles and Nicolas Robert. Parry was excited by this and hastened to repeat the experiment. On 10 January 1784 he filled a large balloon with hydrogen and released it from the lawn in front of the Royal Crescent.

On Thursday 15 January 1784 the following report appeared in the local newspaper.

> *THE BATH CHRONICLE THURS 15 JANUARY, 1784*
> We have been favoured by Dr Parry with the following account of the Air Balloon constructed by him, which was let off in the Crescent at twelve o'clock on Saturday last (10th). It consisted of two hollow cones, joined together by their bases. The circumference of the common base was upwards of 17 feet: the height of the upper cone three feet and of the lower five and a half. The materials of which it was made were taffety (silk) and sarsnet (fine silk), of which it took about (..?) yards of ¾ of a yard wide; it was varnished with the common drying oil of the painters, which is

nothing more than linseed oil boiled with litharge (Lead monoxide). From the dimensions specified above it appears, that this Balloon was capable of containing something more than 72 cubic feet of air, without making any allowance for its approach to a spherical form on dilatation, which, in reality, seemed to increase its solid contents at least one fourth. The inflammable air with which it was filled, was supplied from iron shavings and concentrated vitriolic acid (sulphuric), of the former of which were employed 17 pounds, and of the latter 36 pounds, with a proportionable quantity of water. It was eight hours and a half in filling with air to such a degree as to float, which it did when it was less than two thirds full. It was let off from the field before the Crescent, in the presence of a numerous concourse of spectators. For near two minutes it rose smoothly and with increasing velocity in a direction very nearly perpendicular, after which still ascending it ...? course with the wind almost due West and at the end of two minutes and three quarters from the beginning of its ascent, totally disappeared.

Two hours later another balloon was let off in Bath by Mr Dinwiddie. A week later, 22 January 1784, another letter from Dr Parry in the same newspaper reported that his balloon had landed west of Wells, 19 miles away, after a flight lasting more than an hour.

In a later article (1807) on the decay of wood Parry describes a paint which forms a crust which "is with difficulty penetrated by moisture or air. For this purpose drying oil is spread on silk or linen, in the manufacture of umbrellas; and will tolerably well succeed in confining hydrogen gas, or inflammable air, in the construction of air-balloons."

These demonstrations also excited Jenner who decided to make a balloon and exhibit it to his neighbours. He constructed a balloon which he filled with hydrogen and flew successfully at Berkeley Castle. Evidence for the event is in an undated letter from Jenner to Parry about his proposals.

My dear Friend
I am sorry you can't come among us; neither Peers nor Plebeians I see can shake your Virtue.

Your directions respecting the Balloon are so clear and explicit, tis impossible for me to blunder; but to make it quite a certainty, I intended first to fill it and see if it will float in the Castle-Hall, before the publick exhibition. Should it prove unwilling to mount and turn shy before a large Assembly, don't you think I may make my escape under cover of three or four dozen Squib and Crackers?

I thank you for your kind offer of the Tubes and I will send a Man Thursday next to the Crosslands to fetch them. The Mouth of the Balloon is sadly torn; every other part appears sound.

Please send me by return of Mr Marklove half a yard of such Silk as you may think most fit for the purpose. I have got some oil ready. (Miller G., *Letters of Edward Jenner*, Johns Hopkins University Press, 1983)

John Hunter in Bath

In 1785 after five years in Bath young Parry, aged twenty-nine, was still struggling to establish his practice and to become recognised. This was the year in which John Hunter, the famous London surgeon, made his fourth and final visit to Bath to convalesce after a severe attack of angina. He stayed at 12 South Parade where a commemorative plaque has been placed. He was probably in Bath for three or four weeks and was looked after by Caleb Parry, the youngest and most recently established physician. In the last chapter of his book on Syncope Anginosa Parry writes "It appears, however, from experience, that some gentle and long-continued stimuli have afforded considerable temporary relief . . . I observed the same effect in the case of Mr Hunter." Hunter's choice of Caleb Parry must, undoubtedly, have been on the advice of Edward Jenner, who was a close friend of both men. His attendance on John Hunter could hardly have been unnoticed in a small town, where the newspapers announced and called attention to the arrivals of any well known visitors.

His practice and income were increasing steadily. He was conscientious, and assiduous in his attentions to his patients, as is clear from his case notes. Many patients were visitors to Bath who came with recommendations from their doctors or satisfied friends. Others were local residents to whom in many cases he was called in to give a second opinion by surgeons or apothecaries, and sometimes by fellow physicians. In addition to his work in Bath, Parry made many visits to the nearby country towns. He often took young Charles with him, and Charles records that the calls took them as far afield as Gloucester, Berkeley, Warminster and Trowbridge.

Summerhill

The next year, 1786, was an important and busy one. Caleb's mother died and he inherited the Hillier estates at Upcott, Minety, Cirencester and Tewkesbury. Sir Sydney Parry states that Sarah's will does not mention the estates, but leaves the sum of £200 to Caleb. Sir Sydney thinks that the estates must have been transferred to Caleb before his mother's death. Later that year he bought a few acres of land on the northern slopes of Bath.

His earnings that year were only £552. Did he sell some of his newly inherited lands to pay for the purchase? In the biography of his father, Charles Parry writes – "he became possessed of a farm in the neighbourhood of Bath". Charles did not record how much land was bought. But in his autobiography he says that his father had taken a few acres of land on the north of Bath. The land was a considerable distance from the city, and wholly unconnected with any buildings. Charles writes that the walk from Catharine Place was entirely through green meadows. His father's object, says Charles, was to provide a healthy situation for the family but he saw no disadvantage in putting the land to a useful agricultural purpose.

In his second book[8] on sheep and wool, Parry writes – "In the year 1788 I began to build a country house to which was attached a small portion of land . . . from it's situation it had borne an exorbitant price . . . I was obliged to stock it." No record has been found of how much land was bought initially. In his earlier book[9] he stated that his farm was less than sixty acres, and he described the layout of the fields in detail, suggesting, from the manner in which they were described, that he owned all these fields.

After the land was bought an adequate water supply was found, and there was plenty of stone available on the site. Gardens were laid out, and the architect Eveleigh was engaged to design and supervise the building of a house, for which task he was paid twenty guineas. The house was called Summerhill. Building commenced in 1788 and, according to Charles, it proceeded at a slow pace, rooms being occupied as they were completed. The house appears gradually to have become the main family residence. It was here that Caleb built and enlarged his library, and housed his large collection of fossils and other specimens. He laid out gardens, planted fruit trees, and developed his farm. No plans or pictures of Summerhill to show what it was like when the Parrys lived there have been found, other than a small ground plan in the 1795 map of Bath and its surrounding area. By 1793 the family was able to live there for five months in the summer. The house does not appear to have been finished before the bankrupt Eveleigh had to leave Bath. Caleb was also making additions to the land by purchasing adjacent plots as they came on offer. Parry's friends were amused at the idea of anyone building a home in such an exposed area. But the town was steadily expanding up the slopes of Lansdown, and ten years after the original purchase the scene was quite different, with new houses and streets climbing up the hill. The price of land had risen, and Caleb regretted not having bought more when it was cheap especially, according to Charles, that known as Primrose Hill.

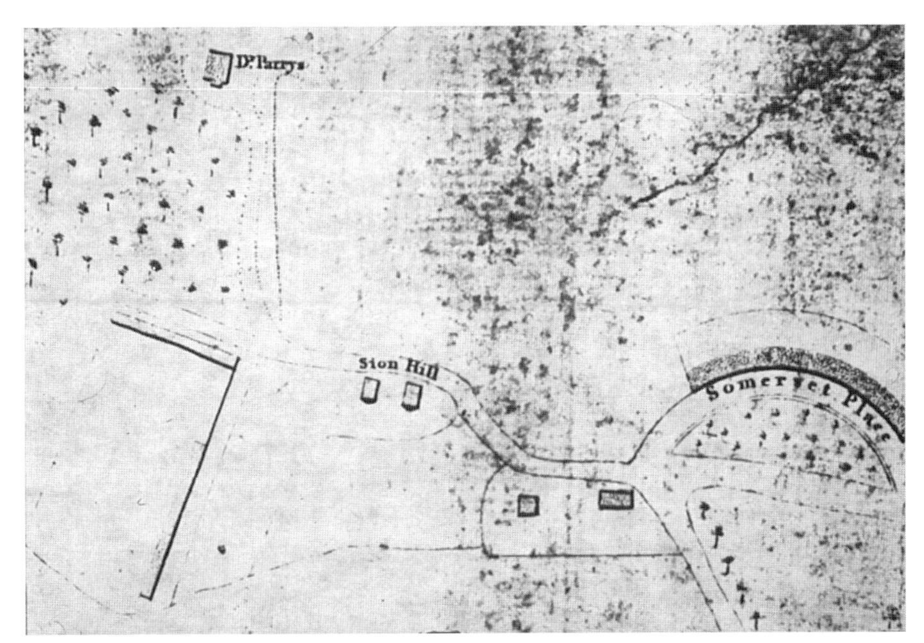

Summerhill *c.* 1789

Summerhill *c.* 1860

The 1795 map shows Somerset Place, from the west end of which a road leads to Sion Hill where two houses are shown. From there a drive leads north to an isolated house, marked on the map as "Dr Parry's". No boundaries are shown for the estate, and there are no other buildings in the vicinity.

Charles Parry noted in 1794 that he was finding it an effort trudging up the hill from the Grammar School in Broad Street, which suggests that the family was now residing mainly at Summerhill.

Publications and Practice

The year 1786 also marks Parry's first medical publication in Bath. Some eight years earlier someone signing himself 'A gentleman from Minehead' wrote to the secretary of the Bath and West Society asking whether it was possible for rhubarb grown in England to be used instead of the expensive root imported from Turkey. After a long and extensive correspondence lasting several years the committee asked Dr William Falconer to test samples on his patients at the General Hospital. This was done with the help of "Mr Farnell, the Apothecary, a very sensible, accurate and well informed person". Dr Falconer also enlisted the help of Dr Parry at the Pauper Charity. In due course the reports appeared. (*See* Rhubarb).

More importantly, however, 1786 was the year he recorded his first case of Parry's disease, "Enlargement of the Thyroid Gland with Enlargement or Palpitation of the Heart", a malady, he says, "which has not been noticed by medical writers".

Sir Sydney Parry[10] in his notes on the family history records that "almost a century after his death, Sir William Osler, the Regius Professor of Medicine at Oxford, hailed him as *par excellence* the authority of Graves's Disease, which, he said, ought to have been called by Parry's name, if any, and took the trouble to hunt me up at our Wendover Cottage in 1907 in order to express the debt he personally owed to Caleb's research work, and his conviction that the world had never appreciated that work at its full value". Sir Sydney goes on to note that in July 1925 "the British Medical Association, meeting at Bath, paid special tribute to Parry of Bath, as one 'whose contribution to medical literature, no less than his skill in practice, entitled him to rank as one of the most eminent physicians of his day'."

His life was extremely busy now, divided between an enlarging practice and a growing farm. He is apologetic about the farm, describing it as a "relaxation from my more serious avocations", and he never allowed it to take precedence over his medical work. For example, when discussing the diseases of sheep, he notes that some times his medical work prevented him carrying out post mortems on sheep that had died.

He was observing and recording full details in both fields, as carefully on his farm as in his medical practice. Charles Parry writes that " . . . in the midst of toil and anxiety, in health and in disease, he never deviated from the plan of recording all that was interesting or important in his practice. At the bedside of his patient, in his carriage, in his walks, or at home, he kept a register of all the facts."

Dr Parry wanted to record the information the same day while it was fresh in his memory. In his own words –

> During the first twelve or fourteen years of my professional life, I recorded almost every case which occurred to me either in private practice or in the chief conduct of an extensive charity. When, afterwards, the multiplication of common examples seemed to me an unnecessary waste of inestimable time, which might be profitably employed, I contented myself with the more useful task of recording chiefly such cases, or, on a few occasions, such particular circumstances only of cases as led to the establishment of principles. This I have generally done on the spot, or rarely deferred beyond the day of observation. . . .

His notes are remarkable for their clarity and detail. They were intended to form the basis of a comprehensive textbook of medicine. Hatton,[11] writing in 1925, stated that Parry's notebooks were "carefully preserved" at the Royal United Hospital, but they appear to have disappeared without trace. However, a large collection, several hundreds, of detailed case records form the basis of his later publications. As will be seen later Parry's extensive contributions to Medicine fall into three main categories. There are major works in which he deduced general conclusions from his clinical observations, e.g. the recognition of coronary insufficiency as the cause of angina; or the series of physiological experiments on the nature of the pulse. There are groups of case records in which he recognised similarities in patients' symptoms, leading him to define specific syndromes such as Thyrotoxicosis. And finally there are remarkably clear case reports which have since been recognised as the first or the most complete early description of some rare condition. It is remarkable how many original contributions Parry made. He became a Licenciate of the Royal College of Physicians in London on 30 September 1788.

The Fleece Medical Society

Earlier, Parry, Jenner and three close friends, John Hickes of Gloucester (later of Bristol), Thomas Paytherus of Ross (later of London), and Daniel Ludlow of Sodbury, formed the Gloucestershire Medical Society, later nicknamed the Medico-convivial by Jenner, but usually referred to as the Fleece Medical Society. There were various bonds which brought them together. Jenner, Hickes, and Parry, though of different ages were all pupils at the Cirencester Grammar School and overlapped in time. The latter two went to Edinburgh to study medicine, and were there together for some of the time, though Hickes qualified MD two years before Parry. Daniel Ludlow Junior was the son of Mr Daniel Ludlow of Sodbury with whom Jenner may have worked when he was apprenticed to Mr Hardwick. Thomas Paytherus's history is less certain, but he practised first in Gloucester and then in Ross-on-Wye where Jenner assisted him with the post mortem on his case of angina pectoris.[12]

Fortunately the Minutes of the Society have been preserved.[13] They came into the possession of Dr Alfred Henry Carter of Birmingham, and an account was published in the *B.M.J.* in 1896.[14] Later Sir William Osler bought them. In a letter in 1915 to H.B. Jacobs, Osler wrote, "Did I tell you that I have got the minutes of the Medical Society that Jenner and Parry founded . . .".[15] In 1928 he bequeathed them to the Royal College of Physicians.

There is no firm evidence as to who had the idea of forming the society, but it is generally believed to have been Jenner, who was friendly with all the other four. Parry, young and enthusiastic, already with experience of committee work at Edinburgh, may well have been the catalyst.

The Society met three times a year at the Fleece Inn at Rodborough near Stroud, a thirty-mile journey by carriage or on horseback for Parry. The meetings were held in the summer months, when the days were long, the evenings light, and the roads passable. At a preliminary meeting in May 1788 the regulations were drawn up and signed, Parry's name heading the list. He was elected as the first President and was in the chair for the first meeting.

The first medical meeting was held on 30 July, 1788. All five members were present. Parry read "part of an introductory address to the Society, on the best mode of conducting medical enquiries . . . and also a case and dissection of the Angina Pectoris, or Syncope Anginosa; together with a disquisition on the Symptoms, Pathology, prevention and cure of that disorder". Parry's second paper forms part of the first chapter of his book on Syncope Anginosa. Dr Hickes and Dr Jenner also read short papers.

In September 1788 Parry was absent and was fined. No business was conducted. In May 1789 Parry again took the chair. Dr Hickes reported a case of perforated duodenal ulcer, and Parry read a paper on the subject of "Involuntary Nocturnal Emissions."

In July of the same year Jenner presented a paper on ". . . a disease of the Heart following acute Rheumatism . . ." and it was followed by another paper from Parry entitled "Some remarks on the Scarlatina Anginosa as it appeared at Bath in the years 1787–1788; with an account of an unusual termination of that disease". This, like most of the papers given to the Society, was neither recorded in full in the minutes nor published.

At the next meeting in September 1789 Mr Paytherus "read a case and dissection of a patient who died of Angina Pectoris". [This is thought to be the case referred to by Jenner in his letter to Parry[16].] Dr Parry read a paper entitled "Remarks on the Typhus and Synochus (continued fever); with a successful method of stopping the progress of the former of those diseases within the first four days".

At the first session in June 1790 there was only one paper. "Dr Parry read a paper which had been presented in 1789 to the Medical Society at Bolt Court, Fleet Street, London, on the effects of compression of the arteries in various diseases and particularly in those of the head; with hints towards a new mode of treating Nervous Disorders".[17, 18] This paper had been awarded a Silver Medal by the Medical Society of London, and was published in the Society's Memoirs in 1792. He delivered another paper on the same subject to the Royal Society in 1810 which was published in their *Transactions* the following year.

This was the last recorded contribution made by Parry to the Society. Meetings continued, though less regularly, until 1793 when the Society ceased to exist.

Edmund Burke

Caleb Parry was keen that his son Charles should follow him into practice in Bath. Charles relates[19] that as early as his tenth year he made many excursions with his father, to Gloucester and Berkeley, and also to the Fleece Inn at Rodborough, where in 1789 he first met Edward Jenner. Jenner took a kindly interest in Caleb's eldest son and befriended him in later years when Charles settled in Cheltenham.

Charles reports that as they were leaving the meeting in September 1789, a gentleman, unable to procure horses, obtained Caleb's permission to accompany him in his carriage. He was Richard Burke, brother of Edmund Burke, who later became both friend and patient of Caleb.

No record has been found of Parry's first meeting with Edmund Burke. In his autobiography Charles noted that he went with his father to Beaconsfield to visit Burke, but gives no details. However there are references to their relationship as doctor and patient in the Collection of Burke's correspondence.[20] In 1796 Mrs John Crewe wrote to Earl Fitzwilliam enclosing a letter she had received from Dr Parry about Edmund Burke. And later in another letter Parry is praised for treating Burke not only with medical skill but with tenderness and understanding. In January 1797 Burke wrote to Parry thanking him for his successful attention, and warning him that he was coming back to Bath – "I shall tell you more fully the history of the decline and fall not of the Roman Empire, but the Kingdom of Me". He was complaining of wasting and weakness. From Bath, Burke wrote to William Windham in February and a few days later to French Laurence. He was so weak that he could not walk unaided from his couch to his bed, but he was "perfectly satisfied with my physician, both in skill and profession, but nature is too strong for him". In March he wrote to Earl Fitzwilliam saying that he was worse and was now in a state of extreme emaciation, but what benefit he had, had arisen from Dr Parry's treatment. In May 1797 he reported to French Laurence that his physician did not expect any further good from the treatment in Bath, and he proposed going home, where he died on 8 July 1797.

In his reminiscences[21] Caleb recalled his association with Burke.

> Of Mr Burke I saw a great deal during a long medical attendance. He was perhaps the greatest man this world ever saw. His eloquence was like a torrent, or like a flame which burns and destroys all it reaches. In common conversation he spoke for hours together as if he had carefully studied every syllable. Not a word was misplaced, and you could never find one equal to that which he selected, whether the illustrious husbandman descanted on the superior excellence of a crop of carrots, or debated in the Senate the happiness of an entire people.

Growth of Practice

In 1788 Mr James Norman founded the Casualty Hospital in Kingsmead Square, and Caleb Parry was elected as Physician. He resigned from the staff of the Pauper Charity and in 1792, when the

Puerperal Charity was formed, he became the first physician with Mr James Norman as surgeon.

By 1789 he was earning about £300 a month, a large amount. His usual fee was one guinea. To earn £300 he would have had to make about ten visits per day and, judging from his notes, few of the visits could have been brief. In addition to his private practice and his attendance at the three hospitals which he served, he saw many poor patients whom he did not charge a fee. Charles Parry writes – "In the year 1805, besides a continued service at public charities, he had given private attendance to 30,000 indigent persons in the city of Bath and its neighbourhood." This statement must be an error. It would be impossible for anybody to see 30,000 patients in one year. Probably Charles intended to write "up to the year 1805" which means that Caleb Parry saw over a thousand patients free each year from 1779 to 1805.

There does not appear to be any basis for the frequently repeated anecdote that Parry had earned one hundred guineas on one day. Charles, who examined his father's accounts after Caleb's death, does say that on one exceptional day his father earned fifty guineas.

Parry was working long hours, often a twelve to fourteen hour day, which was not surprising with three hospitals to visit, a large private practice, visits to the indigent and keeping control of the farm. Usually he started his round of visits about 9 a.m., and he continued until dinner, which was eaten when he had completed his visits. There were also the country visits, meetings, and occasional trips to London. He also found time to read extensively, write and continue his research.

Whenever one of his patients died, Parry tried to obtain permission for a post mortem dissection. If granted, the examination had to be done when it could be fitted in to the day's programme. Some of his case notes record post mortem examinations as early as 6.30 a.m. or as late as 10.00 p.m. He did not do his own dissections. As was customary at that time, the actual post mortem was performed by a surgical colleague. The colleague whose name appears most frequently in the records was George Norman, the son of James Norman who had founded the Casualty Hospital. Parry was always present, and often there were other observers in attendance.

Property Speculation

In 1792 Parry sold the Hillier properties which he had inherited six years earlier, enabling him to buy the Myaconi Creek property in Demarara in British Guiana. In 1791 Charles went to London with his father where they stayed for several days with his uncle George in his chambers, where business matters were discussed. Frederick had not made a success of his legal career, and when the Guiana property was bought in 1792, he gave up his legal practice and went out to South America to manage the estate. The speculation was a failure, Caleb suffered heavy losses and, according to Sir Sydney Parry, was left with heavy debts. George Frederick died in Guiana. Years later, Sir Sydney's brother Edward, who became Bishop of Guiana, searched for Frederick's grave but was unable to trace it.

Parry was also speculating in property nearer home, in Bath, where rapid expansion of the city was occurring. In 1788 according to Ison,[22] he and Dr John Simon bought land which they then leased for the building of Camden Crescent, and from which they received a steady income from the ground rents.

Jenner

When by 1792 the fatigues of general practice had become irksome, Jenner decided to confine himself to practising as a physician and to spend the greater part of the year at Cheltenham. This change meant that he had to acquire the MD degree. The Senate of the University of St Andrews was prepared to grant this degree on the recommendation of two physicians, and his old friends J.H. Hickes MD of Gloucester and C.H. Parry MD of Bath provided the support he needed.

Jenner was very ill in late 1794 with a severe fever diagnosed as "typhus". Once again his friends rallied round, and Parry came all the way from Bath to see him. Jenner wrote to Henry Sharpnell "Dr Parry was with me from Bath five times, Dr Hickes and Dr Ludlow as many, and my friend George (Jenner) was never absent from my bedside".[23]

In 1798 Jenner published his short but great work *An Inquiry into the Causes and Effects of the Variolae Vaccinae*. He dedicated it "to C H Parry MD at Bath" from "Your sincere friend, Edward Jenner". The Wellcome Institute has a manuscript copy with corrections by Caleb Parry, but Baron reports that Jenner read it to several friends before publishing it. Indeed even young Charles Parry claimed that, when Jenner came to London in 1797, he saw him almost daily and assisted in revising his manuscripts.

A later volume, *Further Observations etc.* 1799, was also dedicated to Caleb Parry.[24]

Home Life

Little is known about the domestic arrangements and family life of the Parrys. How, for example, was life divided between the country and town houses? Life split between two houses about a mile apart could have been very complicated. An enlarging and growing family must have found 13 Catharine Place very crowded. Charles Parry recorded that Summerhill was occupied as rooms became available, and later he described his climbing up the hill from school. Summerhill was probably a larger house than 13 Catharine Place. Unfortunately there do not appear to be plans of the original house, which probably became the main residence, especially as Caleb's farming activities increased. The farm started with dairying and the farmer found it required more attention than he could give it. But even when he changed to breeding sheep for wool, it would have been easier to manage if he had lived on the farm.

The problem of managing two houses must have rested on the shoulders of Caleb's wife, Sarah. As the children grew up, the boys went to school, and the girls were probably educated at home.

When her daughters were older, Sarah frequently took them away to visit relatives. They stayed with her brother Dr Rigby at Norwich, or her sister Mrs Bunny at Newbury. Sometimes they went to stay with close friends, such as the Herschels who, after they left Bath, were living at Slough. When they were away Caleb wrote to Sarah to keep her informed of domestic details at their home in Bath. A few of these letter are preserved in the Scott Polar Research Institute, Cambridge. The boys also visited their relatives. Charles records that in 1794 he spent some time with the Rigby family at Norwich, and William Edward also met the Rigby's when his ship was nearby. Presumably the family visits were reciprocated, and the family must have entertained their relatives from Norwich and Newbury. We know for certain that Dr Rigby was in Bath in June 1815 because he was present at one of the experiments on the arterial pulse. Caleb's sister Amelia and her husband Sir Benjamin Hobhouse lived only a few miles from Bath and, from the little evidence available, it may be assumed that the Parrys and Hobhouses met frequently.

In 1795 Charles Parry, aged sixteen, left home and went to London to a school at Greenwich. In 1796 he returned to Sion Hill, and in his autobiography he gives one of the few glimpses of family life, and of his father's irregular hours. The following extract from Charles's autobiography is quoted by Sir Sydney Parry.[25] "A more united or happy family could not exist. My two brothers were of excellent and amiable dispositions. Of five sisters, each eminently contributed, by their tempers and manners, to the happiness and union of our social party. In the midst of gaiety, we could nevertheless enjoy our home and our domestic amusements and occupations. My Father's incessant professional avocations alone stood in the way of the enjoyment we should have experienced in his company and of any regular or connected plan of life." The family would not have seen a great deal of their father even when he came home, as there were patients' notes to write, papers or books to be worked on, medical literature to be read, and at times experimental or microscopic work to be done. There was the large flock of sheep to be supervised, wool quality to be assessed, and in due course to be sold. There could not have been an idle moment.

In 1798 a short paper by Parry appeared in the *Journal of the Bath and West Society* describing an exceptionally large crop of winter cabbages grown on the farm on Sion Hill, for which he was awarded a premium.[26] There is nothing of special importance in the paper, but, as in the case of rhubarb, it shows his approach to the problem, and his method of reporting the findings in an arithmetical form. The crop was grown on three acres. The number of cabbages was counted and their weight was measured for eight rows of plants, and from these figures he was able to estimate the total crop. It is only simple arithmetic, but is rarely seen in papers of that period.

In 1799, twenty years after settling in Bath, he was elected to the staff of the General Hospital, which he served until 1816. A few months before this appointment he published *An Inquiry into the Symptoms and Causes of the Syncope Anginosa, commonly called Angina Pectoris.* Two different title pages show that it was reprinted in the same year, after he joined the staff of the General Hospital. Later (1806) it was translated into French (see *Angina*). In this book, after recording Jenner's discovery of coronary artery disease in a case of angina and his own confirmation thereof, he put forward the original suggestion that the symptoms of angina were due to insufficiency of the coronary artery circulation when extra demands were made on the heart. The book also contains the first demonstration that pressure on the carotid artery produced slowing of the pulse – the first record, according to Sir Thomas Lewis, of the carotid sinus reflex. He also described a simple exercise tolerance test – walking uphill. Later he used the stairs in his Circus house. It

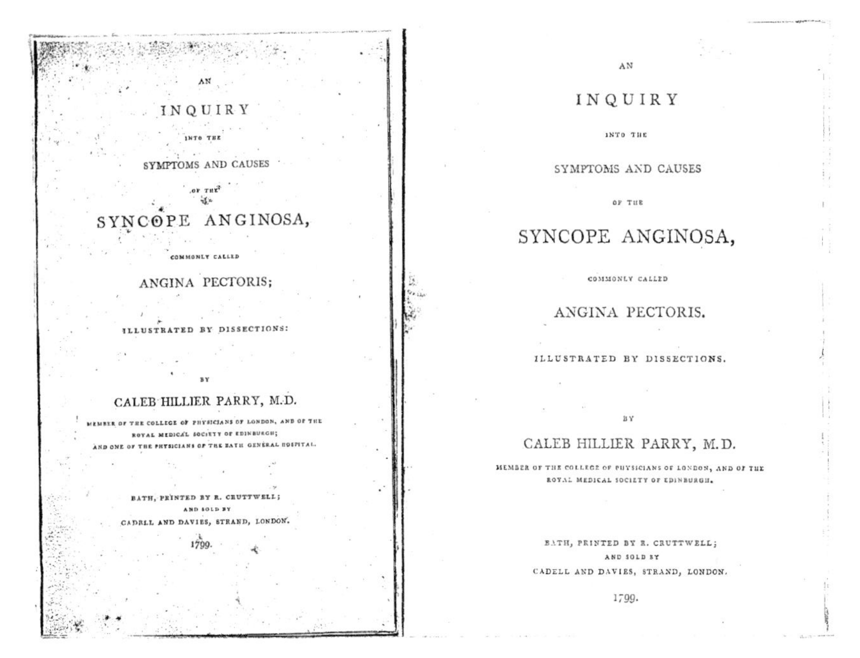
AN
INQUIRY
INTO THE
SYMPTOMS AND CAUSES
OF THE
SYNCOPE ANGINOSA,
COMMONLY CALLED
ANGINA PECTORIS;
ILLUSTRATED BY DISSECTIONS:
BY
CALEB HILLIER PARRY, M.D.
MEMBER OF THE COLLEGE OF PHYSICIANS OF LONDON, AND OF THE
ROYAL MEDICAL SOCIETY OF EDINBURGH;
AND ONE OF THE PHYSICIANS OF THE BATH GENERAL HOSPITAL.
BATH, PRINTED BY R. CRUTTWELL;
AND SOLD BY
CADELL AND DAVIES, STRAND, LONDON.
1799.

AN
INQUIRY
INTO THE
SYMPTOMS AND CAUSES
OF THE
SYNCOPE ANGINOSA,
COMMONLY CALLED
ANGINA PECTORIS.
ILLUSTRATED BY DISSECTIONS.
BY
CALEB HILLIER PARRY, M.D.
MEMBER OF THE COLLEGE OF PHYSICIANS OF LONDON, AND OF THE
ROYAL MEDICAL SOCIETY OF EDINBURGH.
BATH, PRINTED BY R. CRUTTWELL;
AND SOLD BY
CADELL AND DAVIES, STRAND, LONDON.
1799.

Syncope Anginosa

To
Henry Revell Reynolds, M.D.
&c. &c.

Dear Sir,
In dedicating to you the following Essay on the Syncope Anginosa, I embrace the best opportunity of acknowledging professional obligations to you, which it is out of my power to return; and of assuring you of the sincere attachment, with which

I am,
Dear Sir,
Your obedient Servant,
C.H. Parry.
Bath
Oct. 31, 1799.

Henry Revell Reynolds MD (1745–1811) was one of the most important physicians in London from 1772 onwards and is particularly associated with his attendance of George III from 1797. (Munk) He was physician to the Middlesex Hospital from 1773 to 1777. It was during the latter two years of this period that Parry was a student living with Dr Denman, who was also on the staff of the Middlesex. Parry may have met Reynolds and may have attended his hospital rounds. This may be why he consulted him, either for himself or his family, during 1799, between the two printings of his book. But no account of a family illness nor any other reason for the "professional obligations" has been found.

is difficult to believe that it was more than one hundred years before the concept of coronary circulation insufficiency was accepted by the medical profession.

The next year, 1800, he left Catharine Place, where he had spent more than half his active clinical life, and moved to 27 Circus.

CHAPTER 3

27 Circus, 1800–1817

27 Circus

At the end of the eighteenth century Bath was still at its zenith as a social centre, a spa, and a medical centre. The drift of fashionable society away from Bath to Brighton, to which it was attracted by the Prince Regent and his circle, had not yet affected the town seriously. In 1800, according to Warner,[1] the population had grown to about 23,150. The main parish, Walcot, had 14,000 inhabitants, and the rest were divided among the three other parishes – St Michael 3,400, St James 3,300, and St Peter and St Paul 2,450. But for a large part of the year the local resident population was greatly increased by visitors.

The town was well supplied with medical practitioners. The Bath Directory for 1800[2] gives their number and categories. There were twenty-two physicians (i.e. university graduates with the M.D. degree), fourteen surgeons, four surgeon dentists, ten surgeon apothecaries, fourteen apothecaries, four apothecary druggists, and nine druggists. There were several hospitals and charities – the General Hospital, the Pauper Charity whose name had been changed to the Bath City Infirmary and Dispensary, the Casualty Hospital, and the Puerperal Charity. Caleb Parry's appointments to these institutions have already been noted. The most important change was his appointment in 1799 to the staff of the General Hospital, the largest and the main medical institution in Bath.

In 1800, either because 13 Catharine Place was too small for his family and practice, or because the address was not sufficiently important, he moved to 27 Circus. Until the middle of the twentieth century the Circus remained the "Harley Street" of Bath. It is impossible to deduce from the rate book whether he rented or owned the house. The indirect evidence suggests that he owned it. Some time after Dr Parry's death, his son Charles, who had taken over 27 Circus and Summerhill, decided to sell the latter. With that in mind, he moved his family into the Circus. However, as he was unable to sell Summerhill he moved the family back and he reports that he "disposed of" (? sold) 27 Circus.

The Circus house was considerably larger than 13 Catharine Place, but by now the main home was at Summerhill. Parry must have maintained some sort of establishment in 27 Circus but there is no evidence of how large it was. It is clear, from occasional remarks in his patients' notes that he used the Circus for consultations; for example ". . . after walking uphill to my house in the Circus".[3] And he most probably used the large front room on the first floor as a consulting room; ". . . walking up stairs to see me".[4] He probably saw most of the less serious cases at the Circus, and reserved visits for the really ill patients and the titled nobility. His notes show that he often made several visits on the same day to those very ill patients whose condition worried him.

Parry's occupation of 27 Circus is commemorated by a plaque over the doorway. In 1922 the Mural Tablet Committee placed a plaque over the door commemorating his son Admiral Sir Edward Parry. However, in 1925, when the British Medical Association held its annual meeting in Bath, it was remembered that Admiral Parry's father had been a very distinguished physician, and the plaque was replaced at a second public ceremony by the present one commemorating both. Sir Sydney Parry was invited on both occasions but was unable to attend either.

The family in Bath was smaller now. The two older sons, Charles and Frederick, were abroad at Gottingen, where they were pursuing their education. Edward, the youngest son, had joined the Navy in 1803 at the age of thirteen.[5] Over the next few years most of the daughters left home to be married. The unmarried Sarah Matilda and Gertrude Trevor remained with their parents.

In 1800 Parry was elected to the Fellowship of the Royal Society. It is tempting to assume that this was in recognition of his book on angina in 1799, or possibly even his book on sheep in 1800. However, it appears that candidates for the Fellowship did not have to produce any outstanding work to be elected. That requirement was not introduced until 1847.[6] The candidate had to be supported and recommended by friends who were already Fellows, and had to be elected by ballot. Parry's citation reads – "Caleb Hillier Parry MD Physician at Bath a gentleman well versed in various branches of natural knowledge being desirous of becoming a Member of the Royal Society we whose names are undersigned do of our personal knowledge recommend him as deserving of that Honour. Read 20th February 1800 Ballotted for election 22 May 1800."

It was signed by fifteen Fellows, including such familiar names as Benjamin Hobhouse (his brother-in-law), Everard Home, William Herschel, and John Abernethy.

It is interesting to note that his son Charles was also elected to the Fellowship in 1812, and in 1821 the year before Caleb's death his youngest son William Edward also became a Fellow. For a short time all three male Parrys were Fellows of the Royal Society.

Parry was very ambitious on behalf of his eldest son Charles Henry, and planned to have him join and follow him in his practice in Bath. While Charles was studying at Gottingen he became friendly with Professor Blumenbach and his son, and he translated a treatise on fevers by Gottfried Reich, to which his father added an appendix.[7] Reich's treatment consisted largely of giving his patients various acids to drink. Parry's article tactfully refuted some of the claims and suggested a modified and less heroic regime. It is probable that through the contact with Charles, Professor Blumenbach learned about Parry and his works. This may have led in 1801 to Parry being elected a member of the Society of Natural History at Gottingen.[8]

During the twenty-one years at 13 Catharine Place, Caleb Parry had collected detailed notes on a very large number of medical patients. The following sixteen years at 27 Circus were also years of intense hard work and study, years in which he amassed more clinical information.

His main interest, his 'serious avocation' as he calls it, continued to be his medical practice, but he was also carrying out breeding experiments on sheep to produce fine wool, and he was looking after a large and busy farm. Fortunately he was a strong robust man and for many years was able to maintain the pace. Most of his publications appeared during the time he occupied 27 Circus.

Parry's evenings must have been quite as busy as his days. Many of the case notes describe evening visits to ill patients. Sometimes post mortem examinations were done in the evenings, and in his account of his own attacks of renal stones he describes how he was still working at his microscope at 2 am. He must have done the writing of his books and papers at night. This work entailed extensive reading not only of the available medical literature, but also agricultural matters. His works show a wide knowledge of the early literature. In each subject he gives an extensive review of earlier writers, at least all that could be fully researched allowing for his distance from London or a University, an inconvenience he complains about in the preface of his 1807 book on the *Nature Produce etc of the Merino Breed of Sheep*.

Charles Parry writes of his father "Dr Parry was an indefatigable reader. Besides a continued attention to more severe subjects, he had an intense pleasure in the perusal of works relating to history, voyages, and travels". He was also interested in art and music, and had a fine singing voice. His profession brought him into close contact with many important political, naval and military figures. As a result he became keenly interested in naval and military history, and, because of his son Edward, his interest extended to Polar exploration.

Dr Parry's extensive practice was made up largely of patients from Bath and from the country towns and villages around Bath, but it also included many visitors to the spa. Many of the noble and notable from other parts of the country came to consult him. Charles says "It appears that during this period nearly the whole catalogue of British nobility and many of the most distinguished men in the kingdom visited Bath for his advice, and, in their preserved correspondence testify the benefits which they had received from his skill and attention."

Dr Parry's large collection of lucidly written case notes gives an excellent account of how he treated his patients, but these notes cover only the more serious cases. Fortunately it is possible to get an objective account, a glimpse, of how he treated less important illnesses in more important patients. In her letters to her sister, Cassandra, Jane Austen gives an account of Dr Parry's attendance on her friends, the Bridges family. The following extracts give a picture of practice at that time.[9]

15th September, 1813:

> Dr Parry seems to be half starving Mr Bridges, for he is restricted to much such a diet as James's bread, water and meat, and is never to eat so much of that as he wishes, and he is to walk a great deal – walk till he drops, I believe – gout or no gout. It really is to that purpose. I have not exaggerated.

14th October, 1813:

> Lady B. continues very well & Dr Parry's opinion is that while the Water agrees with her she ought to remain here, which throws their coming away at a greater Uncertainty than we had supposed. – It will end perhaps in a fit of the Gout which may prevent her coming away.

3rd November, 1813:

> I shall now tell you something of the Bath party – & still a Bath party they are, for a fit of the Gout came on last week. The accounts of Lady B are as good as can be under such circumstances, Dr P. says it appears a good sort of gout...It may be rather a good thing however that Dr P should see Lady B with the Gout on her.

6th November 1813:

> Dr Parry does not want to keep Lady B at Bath when she can once move. That is lucky. . . . They are to spend the winter at Bath. It was just decided on – Dr Parry

> wished it – not from thinking the Water necessary to Lady B but that he might be better able to judge how far his Treatment of her, which is totally different from anything she had been used to, is right – & I suppose he will not mind having a few more of her Ladyship's guineas. His system is a Lowering one. He took twelve ounces of Blood from her when the Gout appeared, & forbids wine &c. Hitherto, the plan agrees with her.

5th March, 1814:

> Edward heard from Louisa (Lady Bridges's daughter) this morning. Her mother does not get better, & Dr Parry talks of her beginning the Waters again; this will be keeping them longer in Bath, and of course is not palateable.

Most visitors must have come to Bath with some preconceived idea of the healing properties of the Waters and the Hot Baths. Dr Parry probably prescribed the Waters for hundreds of patients. But the Waters do not occupy a prominent place in his published case notes. Clement Carlyon[10] recalled travelling to Cambridge with an ill friend. They consulted Dr Glynn who was very critical of the Bath doctors – "the medical gentlemen of Bath were apt to rely so much on the salubrity of their springs, that their acquaintance with the virtues of the Materia Medica generally was not a little cramped thereby". "I remember that, when speaking of Dr Glynn, some years afterwards, to the late Dr Parry, and mentioning to him jokingly the above conversation, he replied by referring to his pocket-book, which contained such an array of patients then under his care, with notes of their complaints and remedies . . . not a single case did there happen to be among them, for which it had been thought proper to recommend the Bath waters exclusively."

In 1800 he published his first book on the breeding of sheep for fine wool. This was followed in 1807 by a second essay for which he received a prize of fifty guineas from the Board of Agriculture (*see* Sheep Breeding).

Eighteenth-century Bath attracted many wealthy visitors, and had a small but wealthy local population. Portrait painters, who followed the rich, found many subjects to paint. Few doctors were wealthy enough to patronise the most celebrated artists, but there are two notable medical portraits in Bath. In the Holburne Museum, Gainsborough's portrait of Dr Rice Charlton is a superb work, but the large canvas in the Royal National Hospital for Rheumatic Diseases by William Hoare showing Dr William Oliver and Mr Jerry Pierce examining a small group of patients is better known.

Parry had his portrait painted in 1804 when he was forty-nine years old. The portrait has disappeared, a fact noted by Sir Sydney Parry[11] early this century. Enquiries at the National Portrait Gallery and at the local galleries have not produced any more information. The artist was John Hay Bell who was a pupil of John Singleton Copley R.A. So far as is known he was in Bath from 1798 to 1812. He is entered in the *Bath Directory* of 1805 as "Bell, J.H., Professor of Painting at 1 Wood Street". He did not paint very large canvases and the Victoria Art Gallery in Bath has recently acquired some of his works.[12] Fortunately prints were made from the portrait by Philip Audinet (1766–1837), a line engraver, born in London but of French origin.[13] There are two versions of the prints, which show left and right profiles. There are several copies of the print to be found in Bath. (one of each, generously presented by Miss Ann Parry, is on loan to the R.N.H.R.D.) Among Audinet's later works was a portrait of Sir Benjamin Hobhouse, Caleb Parry's brother-in-law. When replying to an enquiry about the portrait by Hay Bell, the National Portrait Gallery, produced a photocopy, from their records, of a miniature of Caleb Hillier Parry painted by Charles Robertson, which had been sold by Sotheby's on 16 December 1974.[14] Charles Robertson (1760–1821) is known for his designs in hair, miniatures, small portraits, and flower pieces.

Copies of the Audinet prints and the Robertson miniature were kindly examined by the Senior Keeper of Costume at the Bath Costume Museum. She immediately identified the miniature as earlier by ten to twenty years. The hair style differs in the two portraits. The Bell portrait shows Parry with natural looking curly hair, while the miniature shows his hair dressed to look like a wig. She thought that the original coloured miniature would probably show that this pseudo-wig had been powdered. This fashion went out at the end of the eighteenth century, and was an intermediate stage between wigs and natural hair. Unfortunately, and surprisingly, Sotheby's were unable to find the records of this sale, and the present ownership remains a mystery.[15] However, they kindly sent a copy of the catalogue entry. The hair is described as "powdered hair en queue". The Parry family also own two silhouettes of Caleb Parry.[16] One, by Mrs Lightfoot, is clearly of the same period as the miniature. The other, by Hamlet, is dated 1812.

Jenner and Parry continued to meet and correspond. In August 1804 Jenner wrote briefly to Parry from Cheltenham, but it is not clear to what the letter refers. However he mentions Charles Fox with whom he had become friendly.[17] In January 1805 Jenner wrote again from Berkeley[18] referring to the controversy between him and Dr George Pearson, who had become critical of vaccination. He asked Parry to

Caleb Parry, 1804

Caleb Parry, 1804

Caleb Parry, *c.* 1780 by Mrs Lightfoot

Caleb Parry, *c.* 1780 by Charles Robertson

Caleb Parry, 1812 by Hamlet

thank Mr Hobhouse (Parry's brother-in-law) who was chairman of the Royal Somerset Jennerian Society organised at Bath. More importantly however, he noted that ". . . A neighbour of mine died yesterday from a disease of the Heart, which followed two or three severe attacks of Acute Rheumatism. You may probably remember a paper of mine that was given into the Fleece Medical Society on this subject. This and my other Papers are in your possession. If you would be good enough to convey them to me, I should be extremely happy in regaining them particularly that I now allude to; as I am confident many a life is lost by not shielding the Heart, at the going off of Acute Rheumatism, which not unfrequently at that time feels a morbid determination of blood. . . ." There is no evidence that the papers were ever returned, nor is anything known of their fate since that time.[19] However in Vol I of the *Collections* in a note (p. 184) Parry writes "A proof of the coincidence of acute rheumatism with dropsy, is, that many persons, who have had the former disease, die many years later of the latter".

In 1808 Parry received a letter from Jenner,[20] now in the possession of Sudeley Castle, which was written on 6 July. It refers to the illness of their mutual friend Dr Hickes who had recently suffered a severe haemoptysis. Jenner rebuked Parry for his neglect of their friend. "The Dr and Mrs Hickes seem to feel much from not hearing from you".

Baron first met Jenner in 1808 in London but it was not until the next year when Baron was settled in Gloucester that a second meeting occurred. This time it was at the Chantry, Jenner's home in Berkeley. Jenner's eldest son Edward was dying of consumption. Baron noted, when he arrived, that "Dr Parry of Bath was in the house".[21] Edward lingered on until early in 1810. In April his father wrote that this "melancholy occurrence" had thrown him into a state of dejection. Baron says "The shock produced by the death of his son . . . materially affected his (Jenner's) health." His symptoms became more distressing, and he decided to go to Bath to see Dr Parry. Baron, who was supposed to accompany him, could not go. Jenner wrote to Baron on 15 June 1810 and it is interesting to see how Parry treated him. He was "cupped, calomeled, salted etc etc" and he thought the noises in his head were relieved but not cured. He was told "to migrate (? take a holiday), and not to think".[22]

When Jenner was looking after the Earl of Berkeley who was suffering from a fatal disease, "he had occasionally the aid of his friend, Dr Parry of Bath".[23] On 17 July 1810 Parry was called to see the Earl and signed a bulletin on his health together with Jenner.[24] The Earl died in August that year, and a post mortem examination report was signed by Drs Parry, Edward Jenner, and Henry Jenner.[25]

Later that year, 8 December 1810, Parry wrote to Jenner commending him on his skill as a pathologist – "it is your own fault if you are not still the first pathologist existing". He urged him to ignore the anti-vaccinists "For heaven's sake, think no more of these wasps, who hum and buz about you, and whom your indifference and silence will freeze into utter oblivion".[26]

It is clear from this letter that Parry supported Jenner's work on vaccination and his claims of its success and its value, but there is no detailed evidence of how active a part, if any, he played, either in undertaking vaccination or supporting its introduction into Bath. It is possible that his large practice and his farm left him little time to do more than encourage others. There were many active protagonists in Bath. In 1799, the year after Jenner's book was published, Mr Thomas Creaser (a surgeon-apothecary) had proposed the setting up of a society or institution for vaccinating the people in Bath, and a Jennerian Society was formed which, with the help of another charity, the Monmouth Society, carried out an extensive vaccination programme. Later Thomas Creaser moved to Cheltenham where he was an active supporter of Jenner. Baron records[27] that as early as 1802 Jenner referred to a paper written by Dr Stewart Crawford in support of vaccination. Dr Crawford became Physician to the Bath City Infirmary and Dispensary, in 1803. Dr Haygarth, who had come to Bath from Chester, was another active supporter of vaccination. Baron also quotes a letter written by Jenner to James Moore in 1810[28] in which he states "My friend Dr Parry, of Bath, has made some interesting observations on these modifications or varieties of variola". Evidently Parry and his colleagues in Bath were giving Jenner their full support.

Lord Berkeley's death led to conflicting claims for the succession, and Jenner was called to give evidence to the House of Lords. Once again, on 19 March 1811, he wrote to his friend Parry to describe his anxieties, and noted that he had received a visit from Charles Parry.[29] According to Saunders[30] Parry was among a group of local witnesses who were also questioned about Lady Berkeley's marital status. Saunders gives an interesting and detailed account of this case and of Jenner's part as the main medical witness.

Parry was interested in everything around him. In 1804 the Bath and West Society offered a premium of three guineas to the person who could propose a cheap effective way of preventing the decay of wood. There is no note of what response was obtained from the members, nor does the prize appear to have been given. But in 1807 a long paper by Caleb Parry appeared in the Bath Society's Papers.[31] As no prize was given, one may assume that Parry's paper merely recorded facts well known to builders and passed on from master to apprentice without ever having been written down. His paper is not sprinkled with references to other writers, unlike his other works of which they are a feature. It is interesting to note that he recommended the value of cavity walls with insulation in the cavity.

In 1812, his trustees granted leases for building on a piece of land to the east of Summerhill.[32] The ground rent for the individual plots was £8 per annum, and was divided equally, £2-13-4 each, between Caleb Hillier Parry, the landlord, William Cowell Hayes, the head lessee, and George Watts. This information is derived from a surviving lease.[33] The facade of the beautiful small Sion Place was designed by John Pinch and builders had to conform to this plan. The buildings were completed over the next two years. Later, as will be seen, the rents were inherited by Parry's two sons, Charles and Edward, and were of some value to both. It is not clear why, if Ison is correct, the land was leased by trustees for Dr Parry. No confirmation has been found, but Sir Sydney Parry says that Caleb was spending much more on his sheep than he could afford, and as noted earlier he had lost most of his inherited capital in his South American adventure. After Caleb's death Charles had considerable difficulty sorting out his father's affairs. Perhaps trustees had been appointed to oversee his affairs after the losses on his overseas speculations.

In his account of his father's life and works Charles Parry reports that in 1808 he was elected an honorary member of the Farming Society of Ireland ". . . in testimony of our respect for the author of the useful and ingenious *Essay on the Nature, Produce etc. of the Merino Breed of Sheep*".[34] In the following paragraph Charles Parry commends his father's interest in horticulture especially the varieties and improvement of fruit trees, and refers to "The very voluminous MSS" dealing with these matters. Not only have these not been traced but very few manuscripts of any sort have survived.

In 1809 Parry published a paper on the use of Venesection in the treatment of two patients with purpura. These seem, almost certainly, to have been cases of polycythaemia, in which case this is the earliest clinical description of the disease.[35]

By 1809 Charles Parry was settled in Cheltenham, where he was enjoying the help and patronage of Edward Jenner, who treated him as a son. Charles "detested" the whole idea of having to practise, which he only did as a duty, but he soon became active on local committees, and was a loyal supporter of Jenner's campaign for the use of vaccination. In 1809 he married Emma Bedford, and despite his father's wishes, he returned to Cheltenham. The two fathers arranged that each would give the young couple £400 per annum. Charles saw the possibilities of living on this modest income rather than the servitude of a medical life.

Not many letters written by Parry have survived. Charles Parry describes his father's correspondence as "very extensive, as well on the subject of medicine, as of agriculture, gardening, and other topics". He wrote many letters to his sons, Charles and Frederick, when they were on the Continent, and to his youngest son, Edward, in the navy. Some of his letters to Jenner are quoted by Baron.[36] In 1958 Admiral Sir William Edward Parry presented the bulk of the Parry family papers, mostly concerned with Admiral Edward Parry of the Arctic, to the Scott Polar Research Institute in the University of Cambridge. There are a few domestic letters from Caleb to his wife Sarah and to his daughters, in which there are glimpses of family life and the worries common to most families. For example, he sent a sum of money to Sarah via one of the daughters and reminded her that he would soon have to meet immense bills for insurance, repairs etc. The papers in Cambridge also include the reminiscences he dictated to his two daughters after he had recovered partially from a stroke.

The most complete collection of letters by Parry is his correspondence from 1800 to 1804 with Sir Joseph Banks, which has been transcribed by J.B. Carter.[37] This correspondence records that "in the year 1800 his late Majesty accepted a piece of blue cloth manufactured from Dr Parry's wool, and declared that, from its excellent quality, he would feel a pride in wearing it." He was obviously still proud of his wool and cloth made from it. "In 1813, the Prince Regent and the Duke of Clarence also gratified Dr Parry by accepting, the former a piece of scarlet, the latter of navy blue cloth; both of which they highly commended, and expressed their determination to wear, as a credit to the British grower and manufacturer".[38] His continued work on sheep and wool was recognised in 1814 by his election as a vice-president of the Merino Society of London.

Other notes are also believed to have escaped destruction. Writing in 1925, Hatton,[39] in an article at the time of the British Medical Association meeting in Bath, recorded that Parry's notebooks were carefully preserved at the Royal United Hospital, at that time situated in Hot Bath Street. They cannot be traced now. Whether they were still around and what happened to them when the hospital moved in 1932 to its present site is unknown.

Health

Neither illness nor age slowed Parry's activities. He was now in his late fifties, and was still actively carrying on an extensive and demanding practice, and looking after a large farm. In addition he found time to pursue his other interests, to continue with his investigations and research, and to write more papers and books. He was mentally and physically active in an age when many men were considered old at forty. But the tremendous load of work was beginning to tell. His writings, especially the posthumous collections of case histories,[40] contain references to and sometimes details of his own illness. In some places he described his symptoms to illustrate similar complaints in his patients. An example is his attempt to find a relationship between attacks of feverish cough and dyspepsia, illustrated by his own experiences[41] and those of his eldest son Charles.[42]

Over the years he began to develop gout and refers occasionally to his attacks, but his main trouble was the development of renal calculi, starting in 1806. His worst attack occurred in 1808. This attack is described fully in a long section (eighteen pages) in *Collections* 2.479. The detailed and comprehensive account of his symptoms provides the main material for the chapter on Calculus, which he entitles "Observations on the Gravel, written from my own actual feelings, five and a half P.M. Nov. 12, 1808, after having obtained some ease from a most violent fit, which began about eight in the morning." The account of his illness covers all the classic symptoms of urinary calculi, described vividly, but with little self pity. His daily routine was still as heavy as in his earlier years "In consequence of great professional avocation, I dined at very irregular hours, often not till half-past seven or even nine o'clock eating nothing from nine in the morning till that hour. I went to bed late, and was long in going to sleep. I was obliged also, from various causes, among the rest an attendance on several dissections, to rise before it was light, and was called up in the night on professional business, in consequence of all which my hours of sleep were very few".

The day after he commenced writing this account he "Visited thirty patients before dinner, in a chair one, others in my carriage and on foot." The attack had started five days earlier with "pain in the left side of the belly". After two days his urine was tinged with fresh blood, but this did not prevent him going to a dissection at 7 a.m. The pain was now in the seat of the right kidney and so excruciating that he walked home with difficulty after seeing only one patient. The pain became more violent "resembling what one might conceive to be the sensation of a sword run through that part of the body, and continually moved backwards and forwards". The pain went down to the bladder and was accompanied by the frequent passage of reddish brown urine. A severe bladder pain was followed by cessation of the kidney pain, and Parry concluded that the stone had passed into the bladder. He now had dysuria and frequency, but felt much better.

On the 14th, after visiting a number of patients, he had an urgent desire to micturate, and from the site of the pain concluded that the stone had entered the urethra. The next day he passed some gravel followed by two stones, and after "great strangury" lasting for a few hours he passed another two calculi "and became immediately easy". Looking back he recalled several attacks of pain in the back which he "mistook for lumbago" and he is "astonished how I did not discover the nature" of the complaint.

It is in this report that he recalls the attack in 1806. "In the summer of 1806, I was a good deal engaged with the Supplement to my Essay on the Merino Breed of Sheep. This Supplement contained the result of thirteen or fourteen hundred microscopical measurements of different kinds of wool, all of which were made by candle-light, and therefore often kept me up till two o'clock in the morning. This fatigue, added to the constant stooping required by the process of observation, often gave me great pain in my loins, and across the belly, and produced red, brownish, or coffee-coloured urine. These circumstances indicated the existence of calculus." That autumn (1806), after some pain in his left side, Parry passed a few calculi.

He was also suffering at times from faintness and syncope. "I have often felt approaches to syncope, but only once its full power. They have arisen from blood-letting in the erect posture". The other conditions which led to this feeling "produced these effects chiefly, or perhaps only, while my body has been erect." These symptoms would surely now be called vasovagal attacks, or postural syncope.

Dr Parry's health continued to worry him. In 1810 he suffered a severe attack of "erysipelas faciei with acute fever, the passage of a nephritic calculus with great pain and black urine for a week, and the successive appearance of inflammatory gout in my left patella, left foot, left wrist, and right foot".[43] In the section of his book dealing with Cutaneous Affections he refers to the same episode and adds that ". . . the skin of my face, and various other parts, repeatedly came off, and with it almost all my hair".[44] And a troublesome wart on his right little finger disappeared during the attack and never reappeared. He was confined to bed for twenty-six days. Erysipelas, now rarely seen, was a serious illness until the discovery of the sulphonamides and antibiotics. The news of his father's alarming illness reached Charles Parry in Cheltenham on 21 December, and he hastened to Bath, where he stayed for three months looking after Caleb's practice.

Charles says that after this illness his father was never quite well, being constantly subject to illnesses of greater or lesser severity (gout and renal calculi mainly) and he had developed a slight shake of his head. Once again Caleb tried to persuade Charles to come to Bath to join him in practice, but, after "a long and most uncomfortable correspondence" with his father, Charles remained in Cheltenham until 1815.

During 1813 Parry had a "severe indispostion which confined me to my bed". He does not say what it was, but it must have been quite serious. He saw Mrs W. several times after her first consultation in November 1812 until October 18, 1813. "From this period, in consequence of a severe indisposition which confined me to my bed, I saw Mrs W no more". She died on 22 January 1814, three months later, and a post mortem was performed by Mr Norman who reported his findings to Dr Parry. It was unusual for Parry not to be present at a post mortem on a patient he had treated. He must still have been unable to work. His gout was severe, and references to it continue to appear. In February 1814 he recorded the case of a nine-week-old boy "No pulse in the radials was to be felt; but whether any beating of the carotids or heart remained, I could not, on account of gout in my wrists, discover".

It has been stated in a recent biography of Edward Jenner that Parry suffered from angina. No source for this claim is given by the author. No evidence for such a claim has been found, either in Parry's own writings or those of his immediate circle. This new myth has already been quoted elsewhere.

In 1814 he published another book on Tetanus and Rabies which was dedicated to Jenner.[45] His first book on the subject of Rabies was his graduation thesis (see Birth to Bath) in 1778.

Parry never lost his interest in geology. His early involvement has been mentioned already – his collection of specimens as a school boy, his excursions with Jenner to Pyrton in his early days in Bath before he became busy with his practice, their exchange of specimens, and his publication in 1782 of a broadsheet appealing for specimens. He was well known locally for his knowledge and appears to have become an authority to whom people referred geological problems. Rev Richard Warner in the *History of Bath* (1801) quotes at length an opinion he had obtained from Parry on the solubility of siliceous earth in water. In his reply Parry refers to his fossil collection to illustrate some of his arguments.

Parry's reputation had extended beyond the boundaries of Bath. Charles states that his father "had made extensive collections of minerals, rocks, and organic remains . . . He had amassed materials which would have grown in volumes". Although this work was never written, and although Parry does not appear to have written anything on geology other than the broadsheet of 1782, he had become known and recognised to be among the leading geologists in the country. His interest in and knowledge of geology was clearly well known in London. When the Geological Society was founded in 1807, the forty-two original members included thirteen doctors of whom Parry was one. Over the next twenty years the Society expanded, and a further fifty-seven doctors were elected, including Jenner.[46]

Dr Parry also increased his own collection by purchases in the salerooms. John Britton[47] gives a short account of Mr Cunnington of Heytesbury who died in 1810. He explored many burial barrows in the surrounding area and accumulated a vast collection of Roman urns, coins, and other relics which were disposed of after his death. "In the latter part of his life he made large collections of fossils and minerals, and from this new pursuit derived much interest and delight. This part of his museum has been sold to Dr Parry of Bath".

Although there is no firm evidence about Parry's geological activities, whether for example he managed to put in occasional visits to Berkeley for field work with Jenner, there is suggestive evidence. In 1812 Charles Parry noted his father's continued involvement in geological activities. On 5 March 1813 Jenner wrote, "I have just packed as many varieties from my old Rock at Woodford as I could now select, and added some specimens from the Rockhampton Quarries marked thus X – you will also find one piece of the plum pudding stone similar to what we found at Thornbury. You will perceive that the Rockhampton specimens bear a character similar to the Rock of Gibraltar – but I have not yet decidedly met with bone in them. What a sublime – what an awful study is this! When will you come and see me that I may lead you to the Woodford Altar?" This certainly suggests that the two old friends were still trying to see each other to pursue their common interest in geology and fossils. In his book, Rev. Warner[48] refers to the rock strata and to the work of "the very ingenious Mr Smith, of Midford near Bath, which we understand will shortly be given to the world". Mr Smith was the surveyor in charge of the construction of the Somerset coal canals. Parry does not mention Mr William Smith and his work on fossils and strata. It is difficult to believe that he was unaware of it, or of the earlier work of Walcott. It would have been facinating to know Parry's reaction to these findings and whether he understood the implications, or was still faithful to Noah and the Flood. Jenner's letter of 1813 does suggest that he and Parry were thinking about the implications of their work.

After he had sent the "Hamper of Minerals", Jenner wrote again to Parry, 24 March 1813,[49] "In Bath, I think you have men of ingenuity enough to split and polish the Pebbles. It would be a gratification to have a broach, or a Ring, decorated with a *thing or two* from my own sod; or what would be still more congenial, my tobacco Box".

In addition to his geological and natural history collection Parry was collecting a large library. Charles Parry states that his father filled Summerhill with his books and collections. A water colour painting of the drawing-room at Summerhill, probably by Charles, is still in the possession of the family (*see* later).

For many years Parry had in mind the writing of a major work, a comprehensive book which was, among other things, going to elaborate his theory of the general cause of most diseases. He first put this theory forward in his paper in 1792 on carotid compression.[50] Parry believed that most diseases, even many that had an obvious gross pathological basis, were due to "determination of the blood" i.e. the flow of blood to the diseased organ. Usually he was concerned with excessive determination, but he also recognised the opposite. He thought the theory was particularly important in diseases of the nervous system. He planned a work in two volumes, the first enunciating a collection of general principles and showing how his theory applied to the different systems of the body.[51] The second volume, which he never wrote but had "long meditated" was to be "the very numerous cases and dissections, which are the proof of those principles . . .". "I have been able to record a considerable number of dissections, together with nearly seven hundred illustrative cases, which chiefly serve as the basis of my intended work." He was now conscious of his deteriorating health, and in the preface to *Elements of Pathology* states that if his plan is frustrated "the author has great satisfaction in leaving his materials in the hands of a person, deservedly most dear to him (Charles)".

Charles Parry knew of his father's plans and had seen the preface in 1812. Parry was so busy with his professional avocations, his practice, his farm, his geological and literary activities, that Charles doubted whether his father would ever have the leisure to write the book, based on his valuable experience. At that time Charles noted that the extensive material was a chaos without arrangement. In spite of these forebodings *Elements of Pathology and Therapeutics* appeared in 1815, and a posthumous second edition was published by Charles in 1825 accompanied by a book explaining and justifying his father's theory of determination of the blood. Charles appears to consider *Elements* an epoch-making work, and it may well have been so in 1815. Of all Parry's works this is the most difficult to read and the least rewarding. It consists of over a thousand short paragraphs, pseudo-aphorisms or brief clinical observations, and some theoretical arguments.

In 1811 Parry, with the help of Mr George Norman who carried out the necessary dissections, set out to investigate the functions of the sympathetic and vagus nerves. A large number of sheep were examined by exposing the nerves in the neck but the results of this work were not published and details have not been found. However, it was during these experiments that Parry noticed that the carotid artery did not contract and dilate with the pulse. This was contrary to accepted views and Parry at once decided to examine this more closely in another series of experiments. Again most, but not all, the dissections were done by Mr George Norman.

The first experiment took place on 22 September 1814 in the presence of Mr Coombs, and the last, No 27, was on 11 December 1815, and the full account with a long discussion and commentary was published in 1816.[52] The work was dedicated to Sir Joseph Banks. Parry was not the first to observe that the pulse was not accompanied by visible dilatation or contraction of the exposed artery. John Hunter had noted it but his explanation was most unsatisfactory.[53] Parry deduced the correct explanation. He showed that, in the exposed artery, to make the pulse palpable the artery had to be compressed against a hard object. He concluded that at each systole more blood was pushed into the system, and this produced an impulse which extended along the whole length of the arterial system. Sir Thomas Lewis[54] considers this to be the first correct explanation of the pulse as what is now called a pressure wave. Once again, as in the case of the post mortems, Parry, had to fit in the experiments at whatever hour he could. The last experiment, for example, was started at 9.30 pm but abandoned because of "professional avocations", presumably a late night call demanding a visit. The experiment was resumed the next morning at 9.30 am. This was Parry's last major work. Later that year, on 10 September 1816, he wrote a long letter in the *Medico Chirurgical Journal*[55] in answer to some criticism of this book. Charles later continued this work and published a book in 1819.[56] He did not add anything of importance.

The work load continued to be heavy. His extensive and demanding practice, his long hours – post mortem dissections as early as 6.30 am or as late as 10.00 pm, his extensive experimental research and writings would have been more than enough for most men. But in addition there was his farm. What had started as a diversion from his medical practice, had now developed into a large business. The size of the farm including rented land had increased to nearly 200 acres, carrying a flock of about 700 sheep. There was the shearing, grading and selling of wool and also the sale of rams to other breeders, and some livestock to butchers for meat. Running the farm was now a full-time occupation, no longer a "relaxation from his serious avocations". There are no records of the staff he employed. That he must have had a capable bailiff and good shepherds can only be surmised. From his own writings he appears to have kept a very close eye on what was going on and there are detailed records in his two books of the grading and weighing of wool etc. He gives an account of the ill sheep, and even post mortem reports on some of those that had died.

The tremendous work load, his recurrent attacks of gout and renal colic, and the severe attack of erysipelas, were all undermining his strong constitution. As Sir Sydney Parry notes "The older Caleb got the more he overworked . . . and took none of the ordinary precautions in the way of dieting and regular meals and rest." In addition Caleb Parry was no business man. It will be recalled that some years earlier he had lost the greater part of his inheritance by speculating in sugar plantations in South America. The finances of the farm needed more time and care than he could give and, as Charles found later, they were badly neglected. He had also become involved in property deals, and the necessary legal matters had not been dealt with adequately.

One of the few pictures of Parry and his household during this period comes from the pen of Rev. Richard Warner. Writing in 1830[57] he gives an account of Parry's appearance and accomplishments during the years at the Circus. Soon after he came to Bath Warner became a patient and later a friend of Dr Parry. In his book he describes Parry's "majestic person, stately step, and commanding manner; nor were the features of his mind, his vivid intellect, brilliant genius, and capacious understanding; his comprehensive knowledge, and his faculty of communicating it to others, clearly, strikingly, and eloquently, less the objects of my frequent and delighted observation." Warner admired Parry's correct and vivid feeling for the arts, his considerable knowledge of music, his "familiarity with the classics and an acquaintance with several modern languages." "Nor must the uncommon talent be forgotten, with which he occasionally delighted his particular friends. The style, power, and general excellence of Dr Parry's singing will not readily be forgotten by those who have had the pleasure of listening to it. It was the union of the melodious tones of a surprisingly fine, deep, but mellow voice, with pure taste, and nice judgment." He recalls some musical evenings he attended at the Parry home, especially one at which Parry and his friends sang a succession of glees, that special English musical form of that period. Some may have been composed by Parry's senior colleague Dr Henry Harington, who was well known for his composition of glees.

On 24 October 1816 Parry was at home resting after the fatigues of the day, and spending a quiet evening with his wife and two daughters. They were entertaining themselves singing songs by Mozart, Handel and others. About 10 pm an urgent call was received asking him to go to Frome to see a patient. He passed the call on to his son Charles and asked him to go instead. Charles went off to Frome and did not return until the next morning. On his return he found that his father had suffered a stroke which had left him with paralysis of his right side and loss of speech. The family had immediately sent for Dr Stewart Crawford who lived at No 2 Circus. Dr Crawford did what he could to help. One of the physicians to the Bath City Infirmary and Dispensary (the old Pauper Charity), he was younger than Parry. He is named as a fellow consultant in several of Parry's case reports, and presumably was well known to the family and had their confidence.

Baron was visiting Jenner at the time. He "was seized with violent rigors, headache etc." which turned out to be a severe throat infection, and it was decided to keep him at Berkeley. While he was there an urgent message came from Bath telling Jenner of Parry's stroke. Jenner went the next morning to see him and returned that evening – a long and strenuous journey for a man in his sixties to do in one day. Baron writes that Jenner said "He looked at me earnestly for some time, then grasped my hand, and by piteous moans and signs expressed how strongly he felt his situation"[58] Saunders[59] gives part of a letter written by Jenner to Charles Parry comforting him and bemoaning the fact that his (Jenner's) dear relations have died leaving him "forsaken and forlorn".

For months the family, much shocked by the catastrophe, watched Caleb struggling unsuccessfully to make himself understood, a struggle which led to a constant state of excitement and irritation. Not long after Parry's stroke it was realised that the family residences would need to be rearranged. Charles gave up his tenancy of 2 Gay Street and took over 27 Circus and Summerhill. In April 1817 Sarah moved into 7 Sion Hill Place with her paralysed husband and her two daughters.

CHAPTER 4

Breeding Sheep for Fine Wool

Parry inherited his grandfather's estates on the death of his mother in 1786,[1] possibly part of them before her death.[2] These estates had provided the financial backing for his education, enabled him to make an early marriage, enjoy nearly a year's honeymoon in Europe, and sit out his early, not very lucrative years in Bath.

The story of his mother's estates is still a puzzle. There is no reference to them in Parry's books or papers, or in the few letters that survive. His son, Charles, says that his father rarely left Bath, so it is unlikely that he took an active role in the management of the estates, which were probably large agricultural properties. His mother, Sarah, survived her father for thirty-four years. It is not known what she did with the estates during that period – were they managed for her by agents, or did she have tenants who paid her rents? It would be satisfying to know. Dr Parry did not hold on to them for many years after inheriting them. Soon after his mother's death he bought some land on Sion Hill, on the northern slopes of Bath. Charles says that there were no buildings in the vicinity, but there was a good supply of water and stone. [Peach's account written in 1893 cannot be substantiated.[3]] A contemporary note states that Dr Parry's land extended as far east as St Winifred's Well.

It is not clear why Parry bought this land, possibly to have a country estate, "a country house" as he described it later.[4] In 1786 when he bought it he earned £552, and it is unlikely that he could have paid for it out of his income. The purchase was made after his mother's death, in the year he inherited the Hillier estates. Did he, as early as this, sell part of these estates to buy land in Bath? He may have wanted to partake in the building boom that was going on in Bath and the purchase of this land may have been partly speculative. In 1810 part of the land to the east of his house was leased to builders who employed the architect John Pinch to design the beautiful Sion Place[5] now Sion Hill Place. According to Walter Ison he also had a share in the land which was leased for the building of Camden Crescent. Parry certainly was a speculator. He did not hold on to his grandfather's estates for many years after inheriting them. According to the family records, he sold the estates in 1792 in order to buy the Myaconi Creek property in Demarara, British Guiana.[6] This speculation failed completely, and his younger brother Frederick who had gone out to manage the estates died there. Sir Sydney Parry says that Caleb was spending much more than he could afford on building speculations, and this failure left him heavily in debt.

Having bought the land, why did he go in for farming? There was nothing about his parental home or his schooling or university education to create such an interest. He may have looked back to his paternal great grandparents (Richard Parry of Pendery) who owned agricultural estates, or to his maternal grandfather, Caleb Hillier, whom he had never met but whose estates he inherited. In 1786 when he bought the land he was earning roughly £50 a month. It would appear that his fee was a guinea a visit. To earn £50 a month he only needed to make two or three paid visits a day. This could not have been enough to occupy an active young man and may have contributed to his decision to farm. In his second book on sheep[7] Parry himself writes "In the year 1788 I began to build a country house to which was attached a small portion of land. This land was high, of a thin staple, dry, unsheltered and, consequently, unproductive; notwithstanding which, from its situation, it had borne an exorbitant price. Such as it was, however, I was obliged to stock it." The Sion Hill area, as yet undeveloped was already expensive in Parry's time!

He started with some cows and a few Wiltshire sheep. "It was not long, however, before I discovered that a cow was, in every possible form, ruinous to those whose avocations would not permit them constantly to superintend the application of their produce". In due course he parted with his cows and Wiltshire sheep and stocked his farm with Portland sheep which produced excellent mutton but "inconceivably coarse" wool. He says that his activities did not reimburse the rent, which may be interpreted as confirmation that he rented extra land over and above what he owned.

There does not appear to be a firm record of how much land Parry bought originally. He states first that the house he was building had a small portion of land, and second that his farm was less than sixty acres. In 1800[8] when he wrote this, he went on to describe in exact detail how the land was subdivided into small fields, which suggests that it was all his property. Another way of estimating the amount of land farmed is by the simple arithmetic of dividing the number of animals on the farm by the probable number per acre. In one section of his book he discusses the stocking rate or density of sheep and implies that he kept about four sheep per acre. This is the same figure as that given by a young neighbouring farmer with a reasonably large flock of sheep. In 1800 Parry had between 300 and 400 sheep and lambs – too many for 60 acres; almost certainly he was renting extra land. It has been suggested that he rented the adjacent Primrose Hill Farm, which according to Charles his father regretted not buying. This seems reasonable. Writing later[9] in the Bath Society's *Papers* he gives his flock as 443 sheep and 216 lambs supported on 165 acres of land.

The Bath and West Society had been formed in 1777, but did not publish anything until 1780 when the first volume of the *Bath Society Papers* appeared, and also the Rules Orders and Premiums with lists of members etc. Parry became a member in 1782. He was also a member of the short-lived Bath Philosophical Society (1779–87). At these two societies he would have met the most important people who were involved with science and agriculture in the area. He also acquired a valuable connection with a local family. His younger sister Amelia married Mr Benjamin Hobhouse (later Sir Benjamin). This was some time after Parry had commenced his breeding experiments with sheep, but the connection with an important local banker, landowner, and influential President of the Bath and West Society (1805–16) must surely have been of great help.

To appreciate Parry's main work on his farm and to place it in context it is necessary to remember the importance at that time of wool in the English economy. There is little need to stress how important wool was in the economy of the West of England with its country towns, large estates, rich families and wonderful collections of art most of which were derived directly or indirectly from the sheep's back.

In his second book[10] which was the prize essay submitted to the Board of Agriculture and for which he received a prize of £50, Parry gives a comprehensive account of the history of sheep breeding, wool selling and cloth manufacture in England, starting with Julius Caesar who noted that Britain contained "pecoris magnum numerum". In the Middle Ages the wool produced in England was sent abroad for manufacture, mostly to the Netherlands and Italy, and the cloth was re-imported. Few weavers were recorded before about 1300, when riots in Flanders led to some weavers escaping to England. An interesting story quoted by Parry, to stress the importance of wool in the economy, is that part of Richard I's ransom was paid in wool borrowed from Cistercian monks. The system remained much the same for centuries but gradually in the seventeeth and eighteenth centuries as more cloth was manufactured in England the situation was reversed and it is estimated that the export of woollen cloth accounted for at least one quarter of the island's annual turnover. Parry's review of the history of sheep and wool is extremely detailed with extensive references to, and quotations from, early authors. One cannot but be impressed by the immense amount of reading that he must have done for this book. For example, when quoting from Ludovico Guicciardini (1560) he notes "having not been able to procure the original Italian, I quote from the French published by Plautinus at Antwerp in 1581".

An important problem which he tried to solve from his historical research into the old literature was the origin and history of the Spanish Merino sheep. He could not be sure how the name arose and there was no unequivocal solution as to where the breed originated. One old theory that he considered was the suggestion that the sale of a few English rams to John of Aragon in 1468 was the start of the Merino breed in Spain. He argued that if these English sheep were indeed the original Merinos, it was strange that the breed had disappeared completely in England. Also he found it difficult to believe that the introduction of five rams to a country like Spain containing large flocks, possibly millions of sheep, could alter the breed. He would, he says, "as readily believe that the whole ocean could be blackened by one vessel of ink". Another theory he dismisses as follows "this is a very simple and plausible tale, which wants nothing to recommend it but truth". He doubts whether the Merino is a pure breed, and also doubts whether, in the sort of farming conditions practised in Spain, it could have been possible to prevent unwanted crosses with other breeds.

However, it was from these Spanish sheep that the finest wool was produced. English wool was mostly coarse quality and could only be used for cloth like serge, and needed an addition of Merino wool for finer cloths. Large quantities of this wool were being imported and fine cloth exported. Most of Europe depended on Spain for fine wool, and naturally efforts were made to break the monopoly. The first country after Spain to obtain Merino sheep was Sweden (1723) and a large flock of Merinos was built up there, enough to make Sweden self-sufficient. Other countries followed with varying results, the possible reasons for which are discussed in detail by Parry. England was slower in tackling the problem. When it was approached the two main players were King George III and Sir Joseph Banks.[11]

Joseph Banks was a rich Lincolnshire landowner, who had inherited his fortune at a very young age, and who was passionately interested in natural history, especially botany. When Captain Cook was looking for a scientist for his first voyage round the world, Banks offered his services and also offered to equip and staff the complete unit at his own expense, an offer which the Admiralty was happy to accept. When he returned with his remarkable collection of plants and animals, one of the people employed by him to help with the sorting and classification was Edward Jenner.

A few years later, now Sir Joseph Banks President of the Royal Society (a post he held for forty years), he had become scientific and agricultural adviser to George III. His position was a strange one. He had no official status at Court and had no authority over the King's servants even though at times he was considered responsible for their actions. He was bound by protocol and, although he often met the King and had long talks with him, his line of communication with the staff was usually through an Equerry acting as an intermediary. This resulted in frustrations and difficulties.

In 1787 George III decided to create a flock of fine-wooled sheep "for the economic glory and security of the kingdom", and Banks was "ordered" to set up a flock of Merino sheep at Kew. In addition to his other duties Banks now became the unofficial Royal shepherd. The first sheep were obtained from France before the Revolution but the King wanted sheep from the best Spanish flocks. This was not easy as for some time the Spanish government had forbidden the export of sheep. However in 1788, a small number were smuggled over the border into Portugal with the help of Spanish Contrabandayos. [Full details of the King's flock and Bank's contribution are to be found in the large scholarly work by H.B. Carter.[12]]

By 1792 the King's flock had grown and it was decided to extend the project by distributing some of the spare Merino rams. Twelve were selected and given to large landowners. The first recipients in the South West were Lord Bathurst at Cirencester and the Marquess of Bath at Longleat. Banks had been impressed by the early publications of the Bath and West Society, which was the only such society in England, and he allocated it two rams, which were deposited with Lord Aylesbury at Savernake. Between 1791 and 1799, according to Carter, 249 rams from the royal flock were given as gifts to forty-three people, but it was from the ten rams which came to the West that the most useful information was obtained.

Parry writes that in 1792 the Earl of Bathurst (2nd) informed him of His Majesty's plan to introduce Spanish fine-wooled sheep to England, and told him that he had received, at Cirencester, a Merino ram from the King's flock. When he received this information, Parry, who was dissatisfied with his early efforts at farming, reflected on the subject, and decided that the best plan for his farm would be to concentrate on wool production. This would free him from depending on the goodwill of the butchers. He would be able to collect his produce – the fleeces – once a year, and they could be weighed and valued by one of the many local clothiers, with no urgency or pressure.

At the time when Parry heard from Lord Bathurst about the Merino rams, the finest English wool came from the Ryeland sheep (probably South Hereford), whose wool was known for centuries as Leominster gold. Parry quotes the poet Drayton who in 1612 wrote –

> Where lives the man so dull on Britain's farthest shore,
> To whom did never sound the name of Lemster ore;
> That with the silkworms web for smallness doth compare.
> (Poly-Olbion 7th song.)

He realised that there was no chance of his developing a pure Merino flock. He writes modestly "for an obscure individual like me to obtain from Majesty the intire possession of a Merino ram was utterly impracticable." Therefore he decided that he would replace his Portland sheep with Ryeland ewes and cross them with Merino rams in the hope of transmitting the quality of the fine Spanish wool to the progeny.

Charles Parry noted that in September 1793 he had spent a few days in Cirencester with his father looking at Lord Bathurst's farm. It was especially interesting because His Majesty had introduced the Spanish breed of pure wool sheep. "Lord Bathurst had just received a ram from His Majesty's 'bounty' and my father received permission to send some Ryeland ewes to the admired foreigner."

As this was many years before Mendel's work on genetics it is interesting at this point to see how Parry planned his experiment and what results he expected and obtained. He writes that "he assumed the influence of the ram's fleece on that of the ewe as being always one half" and "the admixture of the blood of the Merino ram to be always in an exact mathematical proportion". He forecast the results in fractions of 64. Thus the first cross would produce progeny who were $^{32}/_{64}$ Merino. Back crossing ewes from this generation to a pure Merino ram would produce lambs who were $^{48}/_{64}$ Merino, and so on until by the sixth back cross there would remain only $^{1}/_{64}$ of the original Ryeland. Parry believed that the fifth and sixth generations would interbreed and produce similar progeny with fine wool. In other words by selection and cross breeding he would have produced a new pure breed. Among illustrations he chose to prove his view was an uncontrolled experiment occurring in the human race. When a white man married a negro woman the resulting child was a mulatto. When a white man married a mulatto the resulting child was a quadroon. When a white man married a quadroon the resulting child was a mestizo. When a white man married a mestizo the resulting child was a quinteroon. Children of the next cross i.e. a white man with a quinteroon woman consider themselves free from "taint of the negro race". This view of inheritance was shared by Sir Joseph Banks, who, commenting on Parry's work, reckoned that the fourth cross already had $93^{3}/_{4}\%$ of the ram's blood.

Having set his course, he proceeded to examine the problem thoroughly, especially the Spanish claim that fine wool could only be produced in Spain, a view which he distrusted instinctively. It appeared unlikely to him that fine wool could only be grown "on that small space of earth".

In his first book in 1800 Parry examined this claim critically. He read widely and noted the experiences of growers in other countries to which were added his own observations on his flock. He asserts, he says, "nothing but what appears to me either demonstrable or highly probable". The book is prefaced with the following note. "In order that the Agricultural Reader may form to himself some judgment on what grounds I decide on the points which are discussed in the following essay, I must inform him, that my flock consists of between three and four hundred sheep and lambs, of which about one hundred and eight have very fine wool." In case the reader might think he had abandoned medicine he assures him immediately. "I leave for a short time my more immediate occupation, in order to investigate a collateral subject of Natural History, which has served to invigorate my mind by an occasional relaxation from severer studies."

He discusses the effect of food and climate. The Spanish claim was supported in England by many pamphlets and evidence given before

FACTS AND OBSERVATIONS

TENDING TO SHEW THE

PRACTICABILITY and ADVANTAGE,

TO THE INDIVIDUAL AND THE NATION,

OF

PRODUCING IN THE BRITISH ISLES

CLOTHING WOOL,

EQUAL TO THAT OF SPAIN:

TOGETHER WITH

SOME HINTS TOWARDS THE MANAGEMENT OF
FINE-WOOLLED SHEEP.

CALEB HILLIER PARRY, M.D. F.R.S.

MEMBER OF THE ROYAL COLLEGE OF PHYSICIANS OF LONDON, AND OF THE ROYAL MEDICAL SOCIETY OF EDINBURGH; ONE OF THE PHYSICIANS OF THE BATH GENERAL HOSPITAL, AND PHYSICIAN TO THE CASUALTY HOSPITAL AND PUERPERAL CHARITY IN THAT CITY.

BATH, PRINTED BY R. CRUTTWELL;
AND SOLD BY
CADELL AND DAVIES, STRAND, LONDON.

1800.

Title page to *Producing in the British Isles: Clothing Wool*

AN

ESSAY

ON THE

NATURE, PRODUCE, ORIGIN, AND EXTENSION

OF THE

MERINO BREED OF SHEEP:

TO WHICH IS ADDED,

A HISTORY OF A CROSS OF THAT BREED WITH RYELAND EWES;

DESCRIBING THEIR QUALITIES AND PRODUCE, AND A SUCCESSFUL METHOD OF MANAGING THEM.

BY

CALEB HILLIER PARRY, M. D. F. R. S.

MEMBER OF THE ROYAL COLLEGE OF PHYSICIANS OF LONDON, AND OF THE MEDICAL SOCIETY OF EDINBURGH; HONORARY MEMBER OF THE PHYSICAL SOCIETY OF GOTTINGEN; A VICE-PRESIDENT OF THE BATH AGRICULTURAL SOCIETY; ONE OF THE PHYSICIANS OF THE GENERAL HOSPITAL, AND PHYSICIAN TO THE CASUALTY HOSPITAL AND PUERPERAL CHARITY IN THAT CITY.

MAGNA ET PECORI GRATIA.

LONDON:

PRINTED BY WILLIAM BULMER AND CO. CLEVELAND-ROW, ST. JAMES'S.

1807.

Title page to *Nature, Produce, Origin and Extension of the Merino Breed of Sheep* a committee of the House of Commons, but Parry pointed out that the evidence all came from merchants with a financial interest in Merino wool, not from farmers. He goes on in his book to dispose of the Spanish arguments one by one. Thus he shows that wool of sheep kept in enclosures is no worse than those left to graze on common land. Nor can he find evidence that well fed sheep produce coarser wool. In his experience, food "whether hay, grass, chicory, Scotch cabbage or oil cake . . . makes no obvious difference in the fineness of the wool." In like manner he considers the annual migration of the Spanish flocks, the effect of housing during the winter, and climate. He shows from observations in and reports from other countries where Merino flocks have been established, places as different climatically as Sweden and the Cape of Good Hope, that the wool has not degenerated.

> Were a young European female, with flaxen hair to be left by her countrymen on the shores of the Niger, the very first infant which, after a certain period, she would bring forth, would probably have a dark skin, and black curly hair: and in process of time, her decendants would have all the other characteristic marks of the negro. But would any one in his senses attribute this change to the influence of climate or peculiarity of food, when a cause so much more simple and natural was to be found.

He describes his own experience on his land. The sheep were kept in different folds or inclosures, exposed to all weathers, and were fed as already quoted. He goes on to claim that the quality of wool was as good as the pure Spanish. Thus he believed that fine wool was a quality that could be inherited and was not dependent on climate, food, type of pasturing etc.

It is important to remember that when Parry was involved in all the reading, planning and recording on his farm, he had already become the leading physician in Bath. He was earning £300–600 a month, attending hospital wards, seeing scores of indigent patients, and keeping careful records. Charles Henry believed it was his father's careful clinical training that made him apply the same approach to his farm.[13]

> It was impossible for a mind, constituted as his, to pursue the routine, and to witness the effects, of agricultural operations, without attending, at the same time, to the principles which regulate the science, and which should direct the practice. Hence every walk to his farm, intended as a means of occasional relaxation from severe professional pursuits, gave occasion to some interesting investigation; and every crop became the source of inquiry into the means of additional increase, or of economical improvement.

In his book he describes how he proceeded with his plan. At first, as already noted, he did not have his own ram, and had to send a few ewes each year to local people who did have rams and on whose generosity he depended. Building up the sort of flock he aimed at was slow. However by 1795 he was already sufficiently pleased with the progress of the experiment to show a fleece from his crosses at the Annual Meeting of the Bath and West Society, and he was awarded a premium for the second best fleece (Appendices).

In 1796 the Society placed one of its rams with him, but it died the next year. It was replaced by one lent to him by the Marquess of Bath which he was allowed to keep. This enabled him to increase his flock especially as he noted that Merino rams "were extraordinarily salacious" and "their capacity far exceeds that of our native breeds." However by 1800 the ram was old and he writes "I have some doubts whether I can reasonably expect his services even for the present season." By this date he had received one or two more prizes, and had accumulated enough experience and enough detailed records to write his first book.[14]

In 1801 the Bath and West records show the following entry: "To Dr Parry, the Thanks of this society, accompanied by an honorary piece of plate, for his late excellent work entitled 'Facts and Observations Etc 'and a premium of £10.10.0" (Appendices).

Further prizes followed almost every year, either to him for his sheep and fleeces, or to local clothiers for the excellent cloth made from his wool. Although it was all success in Bath, he did have some disappointments when he sent some cloth to Banks. Banks submitted it to his favourite draper, John Wallace, for assessment and had to write to Parry with a slightly discouraging report, that Wallace had valued it at a lower figure than that given in Bath.

One prize of particular interest was given to his shepherd, Thomas Fowle, in 1808 for rearing the greatest number of lambs in proportion to the number yeaned (to yean = to give birth). Was this low infant mortality in any way connected with the fact that the farmer was also an outstanding doctor?

Parry's first book had not gone without criticism. An anonymous letter signed "Practicus" in the *Farmer's Journal* of 1802[15] poured scorn on the work of Lord Somerville (another important breeder and careful recorder), and especially on Parry for misleading Lord Somerville, for making inaccurate claims and for producing "non-descript wool." Parry was provoked and replied the next month with an excellent and devastating letter.[16] First he rebuked the editor for publishing the letter anonymously, and then he dealt at length with Practicus. The details are not relevant now, but the last paragraph of his letter shows Parry's style at its best.

> One word more, and I have done. Practicus accuses me of "enthusiasm." If by that term he means a strong inclination to propagate opinions conceived hastily, and without due examination, I must tell him, that such a temper is not very consistent with an occupation of thirty years in the study, and a very extensive practice of a profession such as mine. If, on the other hand, the term "enthusiasm" indicates an ardent desire of diffusing, for the benefit, as it appears to me, of my country, that knowledge which I have gained by long and attentive experience, I glory in its appropriation; but I know not why I should thank Practicus for allowing me a merit, which I am conscious it is not in his power to deny me.

He was also now corresponding with Sir Joseph Banks P.R.S.[17] who had recognised the importance of Parry's work and the careful records he was keeping.[18] His admiration was expressed in 1803 in his "Report on the State of His Majesty's Flock of Fine Wooled Spanish Sheep" in the following complimentary terms. "Of all who have laboured to render his Majesty's patriotic views in importing Spanish sheep permanently useful to his subjects Dr Parry of Bath deserves the highest commendation."

The correspondence is interesting but not especially revealing about Parry as a scientist. In the first letter, 26 April 1800, Parry wrote to Banks that, following the intimation that the King would graciously receive specimens of his cloth, he proposed to send them to Sir Joseph Banks, leaving him to choose the time and manner of presenting them. He announced that he had now produced sheep which were $^5/_6$ Spanish, and he hoped to breed future flocks with improved carcasses. He thanked Banks for sending some mercurial ointment for scab. In reply, 19 May 1800, Banks, immobilised by one of his attacks of gout, promised to present the cloth to the King at the first opportunity. He warned Parry of the possibility of his sheep developing mercurial poisoning, showing first as increased salivation.

The correspondence continued for four years, and consists mainly of queries and answers on details of feeding, shelter etc. In a letter of 3 June 1802, now in the Wellcome Institute, Parry recounted the loss of the ram given to him by the Marquess of Bath. Using one of his own rams had delayed his experiments by one year, and he offered to buy a ram from the King's flock. In August he asked from where he should collect his ram together with one bought by the Bath and West

Society, and a week later he received his instructions from Banks. On 13 September 1803 he thanked Banks for the favourable comments (quoted above), and enclosed a specimen of wool. In 1804 he reported the deaths of the two rams, one from paralysis due to extravasation in the brain, and the other from pulmonary inflammation. In the same letter, in reply to a question from Banks, he recorded that he had sold eight rams at an average price of £13-8-3, and sixteen ewes at an average price of £3-13-6.

One of Practicus's main contentions was that England needed good mutton more than fine wool. The Spanish sheep had a very poor carcass shape and size, and were not considered of much value as meat. Parry had already recognised this problem, and in one of his letters to Banks he wrote that he hoped to embark on improving the meat quality of his Merino-Ryeland flock by constant selection and breeding from the best formed sheep.

Parry did not like critics. In the copy of his second book belonging to the Bath and West Society's Library, the following note has been stuck in by the Secretary of the Society. "The Secretary by desire of Dr Parry requests that the Gentleman who wrote the Notes in the Margin of this Book will, either with his name, or anonymously, state his objections in writing that Dr Parry may answer them."

By 1812 several pure Merino flocks had been established and once again Parry's work provoked criticism. The claims made for crossing and back crossing with other breeds were not accepted by everyone, and once more Caleb was involved in controversy. His critics maintained that the fleeces deteriorated with his method, and that only inbreeding (or as it was then called breeding 'in and in') of pure Merino stock could produce the fine wool. Various examples of the value of inbreeding were produced including the breeding of race horses. In the five years since writting his second book he had added greatly to his experience. In a series of seven long closely reasoned letters he countered the criticism of the cross breeding of which he was such an advocate.[19–25] He stressed that once animals were domesticated there were very few pure breeds compared with the wild state. And he produced arguments, almost anticipating Darwin, showing that the breeds adapt and alter to suit different climatic and geographical conditions. The example quoted against him of the breeding of racehorses played into his hands. Obviously his critics had not read his article in the Bath Society's *Papers* in 1807 on the crossing of animals.[26] Because of their value, both on the race course and for stud, race horses had better documented pedigrees than any other animals, and Parry had studied them in detail. From this study he had concluded that most racehorses had a very mixed lineage, and there was little if any evidence for the breeding in and in. He wondered how it could be certain that imported stallions, Arab or Moroccan, or Turkish, could possibly be of pure ancestry. Even if it were possible to trace their ancestry to the age of Solomon "or to the very creation", it was difficult to believe that crosses had not occurred. He showed that often progeny of mixed breeding were better than either parent (as was the case in the ancestors of the champion race horse of that period) and he did not see why his claims that his cross bred sheep had fine fleeces should be doubted. He also noted that sometimes after a lapse of one or two generations, distinctive characteristics, which breeders tried to destroy, might reappear. (Mendel!)

To support his contention that cross breeding improved the sheep he quoted an amusing extract from Daniel Defoe's satirical poem on the mixture of races which produced the true Englishman.

> Observe what, in the language of De Foe, is the pure blood of Englishmen.
> "The Romans first with Julius Caesar came,
> Including all the Nations of that name,
> Gauls, Greeks, and Lombards; and by computation,
> Auxiliaries, or Slaves of every Nation.
> With Hengist, Saxons, Danes with Sweno came,
> In search of plunder, not in search of fame.
> Scots, Picts, and Irish from the Hibernian Shore,
> And Conquering William Brought the Normans o'er,
> All these their barb'rous offspring left behind,
> The dregs of armies, they of all mankind,
> Blended with Britons, who before were here,
> Of whom the Welsh have blest the character.
> Dutch, Walloons, Flemings, Irishmen and Scots,
> Vaudois and Valtolins and Hugonots,
> In good Queen Bess Charitable Reign,
> Supplied us with three hundred thousand men,
> Thus from a mixture of all kinds, began,
> That heterogeneous thing, an Englishman."
>
> Since that period the Englishman has occasionally received a slight dash of the Moor, the Hindu, and the Negro; and yet – no offence to my own more immediate ancestry – whatever, the spleen of satyr may insinuate, all the world is ready to acknowledge that the blood of our countrymen has not been deteriorated by this heterogeneity of mixture.

The controversy continued after his death and is mentioned in Ann Parry's biography of Caleb's youngest son, Admiral Sir W. Edward

Parry of Arctic fame, who went to Australia for a few years as Commissioner of the Australian Agricultural Company.[27] He recorded a conversation with an Australian, John Macarthur the pioneer sheep breeder, whom he had met in Bath with his father. Macarthur still believed that Parry was wrong and that it was necessary to breed in and in.

On 30 May 1989 the BBC's early morning farming programme announced that the Scottish Fine Wool Project was hoping to improve the quality of the wool clip by crossing Merino rams with local ewes. This sounded to be exactly the same project as that on which Parry had embarked nearly 200 years ago. In reply to a letter, the director of the experimental unit suggested that the questions would be better answered by Mr H.B. Carter, who was the expert both on current views and on the history of sheep breeding, and whose book has already been mentioned.

According to Carter the experience of nearly 200 years of breeding in Australia and elsewhere has vindicated Parry's work. There is no longer such a thing as a pure Merino. Numerous trials similar to Parry's have taken place, crossing and selectively back crossing various breeds to Spanish fine wool sheep, and after five or six crosses the resulting animals will breed true for wool quality. The present Australian Merino flocks are products of originally crossing Spanish sheep with Lincolns and Leicesters and are 7/8 Merino, like Parry's Anglo-Merinos. In fact Carter thinks that some of the first sheep in Australia may have come from Parry's Anglo-Merino flock on Sion Hill. Carter has shown experimentally that the volume and weight of fleeces can be influenced by temperature and pasture, but the four breeds investigated all maintained the underlying genetic differences in their wool.

Parry's sheep breeding started with the aim of following King George's objective of producing fine wool, and he did it by crossing and back crossing Ryeland ewes to Merino rams. He was convinced that he had achieved his goal of improving both the weight and the quality of the wool clip, but he had to prove it. Quantity was easy to measure and he recorded the weights of the fleeces and compared them with measurements from other breeds and from Spanish Merinos. They compared favourably, but quality was what really mattered, and that was more difficult to assess objectively. For one thing the fleece differed on different parts of the animal and it was necessary to compare like with like. The Spaniards graded their fleeces into 4 grades of wool and it was the fine grade that gave the greatest reward. Parry devoted a lot of space in his writings to detailed examination of this question, weights of fleeces before cleaning, after cleaning, how cleaned etc, so as to make as fair a comparison as possible of his wool with the Spanish, but in the end the judgement was largely a subjective one made by the wool buyer, who used his experience to price it by feel and appearance. Parry complained about this and said that no three people gave the same opinion when he showed them his wool. He could and did show his wool in competitions and as already noted he won many prizes with his wool.

In the Bath Society's *Papers* (Vol 1807, p. 159) there is a report on "An Account of the Manufacture of two pieces of Navy Blue Broad Cloth for the Premium of the Society". A blind comparison was made of two samples of cloth. The committee had, in conjunction with several Woollen-Drapers of this city . . . compared cloths 1 and 2 and judged No 1 as best. This was from Dr Parry's Anglo Merino breed. The other was from one of the best wools from Spain. Samuel Yeats and Son who had made the cloths stated "Dr Parry's wool and cloth . . . works much more kindly than the Coronet (Spanish)", and "We do not scruple to say . . . the cloth made with the British wool is decidedly of the finest quality."

It still remained a subjective judgement depending on the market. Parry was sure that a method of measuring fineness was needed, some method of measuring accurately the diameter of the fibres and thus getting rid of the purely subjective judgement of the market place. He was not alone in this search, but he appears to have been the successful one. Daubenton in France had experimented with a finely ruled grid or micrometer, and examined the fibres superimposed on the grid. However, as Parry pointed out, it could never be an accurate measure. It was almost impossible to get a fibre lying exactly along a ruled line and, even if one succeeded, unless the fibre fully filled the space between two lines its size still had to be guessed.

Parry turned to his old friend Herschel for advice. Herschel referred him to two papers he had written on the description of a Lamp-Micrometer, and the Method of using it.[28] Herschel had found difficulty with using the grid technique to measure the distances between and the diameters of the smallest stars he could see. The problem was that often the width of the lines on the grid was as large as the stars. His solution was to produce a large external image making it easy to measure and then by arithmetical calculations work out the correct figure. Parry applied the same principles to measuring the diameter of wool fibres.

> An object of known diameter being placed on the stage of the microscope in a strong light, and a piece of white paper spread horizontally beneath it, look through the tube at the object with both eyes open, and you will see its image projected on the paper below, which you may then measure with a pair of compasses, and take off the aperture on a diagonal scale minutely subdivided. Divide this magnified image by the known diameter of the object, and you will find the magnifying power. This being found, place on the stage the object, the diameter of which is sought, and having measured with the compasses, as before, the diameter of its image projected on the paper below, divide that diameter by the magnifying power, and the quotient will be the real magnitude required.

It is worth detailing this work because it helps give a picture of the man and his remarkable application and ability. He found it difficult to get a distinct view by daylight so he made his examinations by night "the object being strongly illuminated by the light of an Argand lamp", or by candle. Having practised the technique he found "that the diameters of any minute objects could easily and with great precision be ascertained". He prepared his specimens by stretching a lock of wool on a slide and waxing the ends to keep it there. He then blackened the slide leaving three clear areas through which he could examine the wool. He measured the diameter of ten fibres in each window. "In this mode, therefore, the fineness of each end, and of the middle of each specimen, is deduced from the mean diameter of ten filaments, and that of the whole specimen from the mean diameter of thirty filaments."

He not only examined wool from his own flock but also obtained specimens from other sources, some from Spain, some from pure English Merino flocks and some sent from Cape Town. His table shows the results in thirty-one fleeces, and he records that he made over a thousand measurements.

Parry's measurements were astonishingly accurate. Mr Carter has found, at the Natural History Museum in London, a sample of washed wool from Parry's estate of Summerhill in Bath in 1803. Translating Parry's measurements into microns he finds Parry's average figure for the diameter was 21.3 microns. Using modern methods of projection and measurement, Carter's figure is 21.5 microns, a difference of 0.2 microns or roughly 1%. Whether this work helped Parry to sell his wool or spare rams is not known, but he was well ahead of his time. Until recently wool continued to be assessed and sold on the subjective judgements of the dealers. It is only in the last twenty years or so that wool has been graded for sale by accurate measurement of the staple.

However, the quality of Parry's rams and of his flock's wool was appreciated and some income was derived from the sale of rams. In a letter of 1809 to his wife[29] he reported that the sale of his sheep was highly favourable amounting to nearly a thousand pounds. This was very good, he writes, considering that the sheep which were sold, were the worst in his flock.

Naturally, as one might expect from a scientifically minded doctor, his book contains one chapter on diseases of sheep, and a second on their treatment. Parry approached diseases of sheep with the same diagnostic skill, keen observation and accurate recording, as he did with his human patients. The two chapters clearly show the influence of his medical training and his familiarity with medical literature.

Librarians at well known local agricultural colleges have been most helpful in finding eighteenth-century references to diseases of sheep, but none has found a comparable contemporary attempt at a complete list of the diseases of sheep. The Veterinary College of London was founded in 1791, but was only interested in horses until the late nineteenth century. Early articles on sheep appear to have contained brief references to one or two diseases only. Most of the information was probably well known among farming folk, and was passed by word of mouth and not written about. Unusually for him, Parry gives no references to other writings, but does make some remarks indicating that he was familiar with the literature e.g. "a disease much noticed by the French" or "a complaint too well known to require description".

If Parry could find the time, he arranged for a post mortem when a sheep died, but apologised for not investigating all deaths. "Partly from other occupations, and partly from neglect of notice by my servants, I have omitted to open the heads of any of these sheep, but I shall endeavour to avail myself of future opportunities of this kind."

In only one group of cases does Parry claim to be describing a condition not previously noted. In 1804 "4 or 5 of my ewes died of a disease, which, though perhaps common enough, has not been mentioned by writers on sheep". "The lungs being examined after death, were found full of vesicles or bladders, from the size of a small pea to half an inch in diameter, containing a colourless transparent liquid. These bladders are denominated hydatids, supposed to be living animals, and called, by Linnaeus, Taenia Hydatigenea". The chapters contain short accounts of the other lesions he came across in his flock and notes on their treatment. The list consists of the following – liver fluke, pleurisy, gid or giddiness, scab, foot rot, scouring, tetanus, and attacks by fly and ticks.

In 1816 he suffered a stroke which left him with a right hemiplegia and affected his speech and brain, and which put an end to his medical and agricultural work. After his stroke, his son Charles took over the management of Summerhill. He was not interested in the sheep, and found the maintenance of the flock troublesome and expensive. He appears to have sold the sheep as and when possible. By 1828 he had reduced the flock from between 600 and 700 to only 40–50.

Parry's final honour was given to him by the Bath and West Society in 1817. The minutes of the adjourned General Meeting, 15 December 1817 state:

> It was also agreed that it be recommended to the Annual Meeting tomorrow to present Dr Parry with a Bedfordian Gold Medal as a small tribute for his eminent Services.

The Bedfordian Gold Medal

The next day (16 December 1817) at the Annual Meeting

Mr Graeme then rose, and observed that if any individual deserved the good opinion of the society, and the public in general, Dr Parry, whose name could not be mentioned but in terms of sincere respect, was that person; to him, he therefore moved, that the Gold Medal of the Society should be presented as the highest mark of their esteem – Dr C Parry expressed his feelings of gratitude for the honourable mention of his father, and assured the meeting, that his revered father would feel the highest gratification in the knowledge that his exertions had merited such a distinguished mark of their approbation. His father was one of the oldest members, and had always a great anxiety for the promotion of the objects, of the Bath and West of England Society. Under these considerations, he was sure that the vote of this day, would afford him the greatest consolation under the pressure of that indisposition, which has so long incapacitated him from the discharge of useful pursuits – This final address was heard with attention, and honoured with repeated acclamations.

CHAPTER 5

7 Sion Place, 1817–1822

A few months after Caleb's stroke, his wife Sarah moved out of 27 Circus and Summerhill, which were taken over by Charles Parry, who gave up his tenancy of 2 Gay Street. Edward returned from Canada, where he had been serving in the Navy, in time to help with the move. Fortunately the terrace in Sion Place seems to have escaped the complications of debt and lack of management. Sarah was able to occupy No. 7 in this beautiful little terrace, and in early 1817 she moved there with her paralysed husband and her two unmarried daughters, Sarah Matilda and Gertrude Trevor. Here Caleb Parry spent his remaining years devotedly looked after by his wife and daughters.

Parry had written his last book – on the Arterial Pulse – in 1816, but the experimental work was continued and completed by Charles, who published his results in 1819.[1] No significant addition was made to the original work. In the preface he pays tribute to his father and describes his sad state and struggles with paralysis.

> The functions of that clear and vigorous mind were suddenly suspended, and the energies of a most active frame arrested in the midst of health, and hope, and occupation.
>
> A melancholy interval of superadded suffering, mental as well as physical, has not tended to the restoration of these powers; and though the mind has so far recovered its tone as to seek consolation in variety of employment, continued bodily infirmity still places a bar upon exertion, and the means of intercourse and communication are still withheld.

Difficulty of communication was Caleb Parry's greatest burden. In his biography of his grandfather, Charles Parry[2] says of his father that his "condition over the next six years amply verified the misery described as attendant upon such a state". These were difficult years, not only for Caleb, but for his devoted wife Sarah, and the rest of the family.

The year 1817 ended with the honour bestowed on Parry by the Bath and West Society.[3] They presented Parry with their highest award – the Bedfordian Gold Medal. He was not well enough to receive it and it is uncertain how much he could have appreciated it. The honour was accepted on his behalf by his son Charles.

Caleb's difficulty in expressing himself, an active mind bound in chains, led him to become irritable at times. Following these outbursts he became contrite and apologetic and often wept. He improved slowly and later in 1818 was beginning to read. That year their daughter Emma Wilmot died in childbirth much to the distress of Sarah and Caleb, especially the latter who was still emotionally unstable and unable to express himself. During the year he had improved sufficiently to be lifted down to dinner and in fair weather he was wheeled into the gardens, where he is said to have made a catalogue of his fruit trees.

Edward Parry came home on leave in 1820 and his father derived great pleasure from the visit and from reading and correcting Edward's manuscript account of his voyage in Hecla.[4] His mental state was greatly improved, as was his speech, but he was still liable to attacks of frustration and irritability.

In spite of all his disabilities Caleb managed to dictate a series of reminiscences to his daughters and a thirty page essay on the character of Hamlet. In 1897 Sir Sydney Parry[5] reviewed Charles Parry's biography of his grandfather, the Rev. Joshua Parry, and also the unpublished MSS of Dr Caleb Hillier Parry, from which he gave some extracts. The original manuscript notes are now in the Scott Polar Research Institute. There are no dates to indicate when any of these reminiscences were dictated. Some concern Dr Parry's more eminent patients as seen by their doctor and friend. One of his distinguished patients was Lord Rodney who "in after-life became very intimate with Caleb Parry, who attended him in several long illnesses. He spoke, says Parry, with great energy on all occasions, and in his conversation had a certain smartness which was not to be exceeded. He always seemed as if he was reciting."

Another naval friend and patient was Lord Howe and Sir Sydney Parry quotes extensive extracts from Parry's notes. As well as the two Hunter brothers and Edmund Burke, other patients mentioned include the Duke of Clarence, the Duchess of Gordon, and one of his last patients was the King of France. There are reminiscences of his friend Herschel, and of some well known musicians, Nancy Storace, Rauzzini and Braham. The Spanish ambassador, who died from jaundice, was also one of his patients.

Throughout Parry's long illness he continued to suffer much pain from his gout and urinary calculi. These worsening attacks often led to more outbursts of impatience and irritability followed by contrition and tears of remorse. It was a great burden on Sarah and her daughters.

After Parry's stroke, Rev. Warner visited him frequently "at his especial request and joined with him in prayer; and in the most solemn rite of the established church." Warner goes on,[6]

> It was there that I saw an improving example of the union of the good and the great in the human character: and a visible proof, that saint-like piety is perfectly compatible, with exalted talent, rare accomplishment, and profound philosophy: and it was there, that I saw, developed in beautiful form and embodied in incessant action, the sacred feelings of conjugal love, and filial affection; vigilant to watch the languid eye, and interpret the imperfectly pronounced word; to guide the feeble hand; to supply the frequent want; and anticipate the wish that could not be expressed.

In a footnote he adds –

> I made some enquiries respecting my distinguished friend, the Doctor's noble son, Captain Sir Edward Parry, R.N., who was then prosecuting his adventurous voyage to the North Pole. The question seemed to throw a momentary light and life into the Doctor's benumbed and exhausted system. He called for an atlas:– a large map of the world was spread before him; and, with his tremulous hand, he attempted to trace out the long and intricate course which the bold navigator had pursued; and the exact spot in which he then supposed him to be.

In 1821 Caleb's health began to deteriorate rapidly and he had many severe epileptic fits. Charles decided it would be wise for him to sleep at 7 Sion Place to be on hand if needed. It was around this time that Edward Jenner spent three days staying with the Bedfords at Elmhurst in Batheaston and he visited his old friend each day.

In the early part of 1822 Dr Parry insisted on trying to cope with some of his business affairs, difficulty over loans etc., and read the details of some of the vexatious and harassing litigation. He became very upset and this led to a severe attack following which, on 9 March 1822, he died. Charles does not indicate the exact nature of the attack, but presumably it was one of his fits.

The funeral took place a few days later. Parry had asked for a private funeral, but as soon as the news of his death was known more than half the doctors in Bath wrote to Charles to ask for permission to attend the funeral. A long obituary appeared in the *Bath Chronicle* of

21 March 1822, which included a report of their request, and a copy of their letter.

> At the particular desire of the deceased, the funeral was to have been strictly private, but the request contained in the following letter rendered it quite impossible to adhere to this arrangement.
>
> To Dr Charles Parry Bath, March 11 1822
> Sir
> We the undersigned friends and professional associates of your late father, anxious to testify our deep regret for his loss, and our ardent wish to pay respect to his memory, entreat that you will permit us to attend his remains to the Abbey Church, and also allow us to erect a memorial there, expressive of our high opinion of his worth as a man, and of his exalted talents as a physician. We have the honour to be, Sir, your obedient servants.

It was signed by thirty-nine doctors.

Following this, and possibly other requests, Parry's wishes were ignored and a public funeral was held. The procession drove from Summerhill to the Abbey where he was buried. The hearse was followed "from his house on Sion Hill to the Abbey Church, by a train of mourners and friends, such, perhaps, as was never before witnessed on a similar occasion in Bath. A vast crowd of spectators of all ranks, to many of whom the person and character of the deceased were familiar, anxious, as it were, to testify their regard for his memory, filled the windows of every house and lined the streets through which the funeral procession passed." The chief mourners occupied fourteen coaches and there were, in addition, many "gentlemen's carriages". Dr Charles Henry Parry was chief mourner, and the other relatives included Sir Benjamin Hobhouse, Sir John Eardley Wilmot, the Rev Mr Garnier and Mr Bunny. Of his "medical brethren, the principal practitioners in Bath, at least forty in number" attended.

Dr Edward Jenner was one of the pall bearers. Baron[7] reported Parry's death. "Jenner was one of his oldest and most attached friends. He went to Bath to attend his funeral, which took place about the middle of January 1822. 'Poor Parry!' he observes. 'I have just returned from Bath, where I went to attend his remains to the silent tomb. The manifestations of regard and affection exhibited by all ranks from Sion Hill to the Abbey, bore unequivocal testimony to his worth and talents.'" Jenner's remarks confirm the newspaper account of the crowded street lined by the respectful sad population.

Dr Parry was buried in the Abbey and his colleagues erected a

monument to him on the wall of the south aisle of the nave, with the following laudatory Latin inscription;

H.S.E.
CALEB HILLIER PARRY, M.D.R.S.S.
Vir Probus
Cultor Dei pius,
Medicus sagax.
Artem qua pollebat,
In hac urbe, per annos fere XL.
Ingenio, moribus,
Multiplici litterarum cognitione,
Exornavit:
Scientia, naturae indagatione perspicaci,
Feliciter promovit.
Ne tanto nomini
Ulla pars observantiae
Desideraretur,
Amici, eadem arte consociati,
Hoc marmor
P.C.
Vixit annos LXVI. Obt. IX. die Mens. Mart.
A. S. 1822.

The April 1822 number of the *Gentleman's Magazine*[8] contained a two page obituary in which Parry's contributions to medical discovery and his general philosophy of medicine, illustrated by his book *The Elements of Pathology*, are all commended especially the last. There is also a special notice of his first paper recommending carotid compression, a principle which he extended later. His other interests such as his work on wool are also mentioned. "His moral, courage, and parental feelings, were exemplary. In a continued series of bodily suffering, his Christian resignation was perfect."

A few months later Charles Parry was among the small group of friends who attended Edward Jenner's funeral at Berkeley.

After Parry's stroke in 1816, Charles Parry had taken charge of his father's medical affairs. He continued his father's practice but he was not happy with the work. He was, he says, overpowered by the multitude of professional duties of "the most obnoxious and disgusting kind". He appears to have reduced the amount of work, both medical and agricultural, and concentrated on completing his father's unfinished writings. Charles Parry knew as early as 1812 that his father had been planning a major work, in which he proposed using his vast collection of detailed case notes to illustrate his theory, first put forward in 1792, that the cause of many diseases and symptoms was excessive determination of the blood. The first volume of the work, *Elements of Pathology and Therapeutics* appeared in 1815. But he had not done much more, before his stroke in 1816, than announce his intention to write a second volume.

In 1825 Charles published a second edition of the *Elements of Pathology*, and later that year he published the *Collections from the Unpublished Medical Writings of the Late Caleb Hillier Parry M.D. F.R.S.* in two volumes. This contained several original observations which are discussed later (See Posthumous Publications).

Summary

The list of Parry's original observations is impressive, and is presented subject to the usual reservations about claims for priority. In his paper of 1787 his description of the symptoms of an hysterical young woman includes what is probably the first report of Tetany due to Hyperventilation. The paper also includes the first description of Histamine Cephalgia, and the first report of the use of carotid compression to relieve the pain of Hemicrania.

His book on angina was the first monograph to be published on the subject. Parry reported the original observations of Jenner who was the first to note the presence of obstructive disease of the coronary arteries in two fatal cases of angina; and he recorded his own confirmatory post mortem observations. He realised that although the symptoms were intermittent the obstruction was present all the time, and he was the first to conclude that the pain was caused by the inability of the diminished coronary circulation to meet the extra demands of exercise. He was also the first to demonstrate this by simple exercise tolerance tests in his patients. This book also includes the first demonstration of the slowing of the pulse caused by carotid compression.

In his paper on Purpura he reported two cases probably due to polycythaemia, the earliest description of the condition. In *Elements of Pathology and Therapeutics*, a book much praised by his contemporaries, the only original contribution is his description of Reactive Hyperaemia. The last book published during his lifetime gives the first correct explanation of the mechanism of the pulse. His collected case notes, published after his death, contain the first descriptions of Thyrotoxicosis, of Idiopathic Dilatation of the Colon, of Facial Hemiatrophy, of Aneurysmal Dilatation of the Auricles in Mitral Stenosis, and probably also of Hay Fever.

His work on cross breeding sheep for fine wool was the first properly documented and successful experiment. He was the first to measure accurately the diameter of wool fibres. No earlier account has been found of the use of insulation in cavity walls.

It is impossible to improve on the words of Sir Thomas Lewis

> Unremitting in his practice as the leading physician of Bath . . . he was simultaneously one of the most renowned agriculturists of his time, and an ardent geologist. These pursuits, and the many social and scientific contacts which they brought him were still inadequate to saturate his energies. The spirit of enquiry was ever present in his clinical work, his observations were acute, his deductions and inductions prolific. His unflagging spirit, his meticulous recording, left behind him for posterity a series of accurately written works and a galaxy of recorded discovery, rarely surpassed by any practising physician within the records of our Islands. His was a truly great, a noble, career; the man remains for us a shining example and an inspiration.[9]

CHAPTER 6

Epilogue

After Caleb's death Charles was left with the task of sorting out and settling his father's estate. Sir Sydney Parry[1] says of his great-grandfather Dr Caleb Parry "his affairs were left in some confusion, and his will (dated 11 April 1820) was evidently drafted by himself in his broken state, and is almost unintelligible". Thus it is difficult to know in exact detail how the property and other assets were divided. Charles noted in 1822[2] that he had become the possessor of Summerhill which had been settled on him, his wife, and his children. No record has been found of what financial arrangements were made for Caleb's wife Sarah, or the two unmarried daughters. However there was no immediate alteration in the living arrangements in Bath. Sarah and her daughters Matilda and Gertrude stayed at 7 Sion Place for a time, and then moved into Summerhill with Charles and his family.

In 1824 her youngest son, then Post-Captain, Edward Parry was in England, and he arranged for her portrait to be painted by John Jackson R.A. The painting is now in the Sir John Soane's Museum in London.

Living at Summerhill proved unsatisfactory, and in 1828 they moved to London to 76 Baker Street. In 1829 the family celebrated Sarah's eightieth birthday. Two years later on 16 December 1831 she died, and was buried in Bath Abbey next to her husband.

Parry had allowed his financial affairs to become confused and complicated, and Charles was faced with many problems. Simple legal precautions had not been observed in property dealings. No titles to houses or land had been prepared. The estate was owed money by many people and no proper accounts had been kept. For years Charles was involved in lawsuits with people he described as dishonest and vulgar with whom his father had implicated himself. His uncle, Sir Benjamin Hobhouse, gave what help he could in sorting out the problems. Charles found the estate expensive and burdensome, and set about clearing the debts and reducing the liabilities. He gradually sold off the sheep so that by 1828 the flock had been reduced from about 700 to less than 50, and he tried to sell the estate.

In 1823 William Beckford was looking for a property in Bath. He had sold Fonthill in 1822 (before the tower collapsed) and had retired to Bath. He was interested in Summerhill and the details for a sale were agreed. However there was some difficulty over a tenant on the estate who could not be moved, and the sale fell through, much to Charles's distress. The agreed price was £18,600, equivalent today to well over one million pounds. No other buyer was forthcoming.

After this disappointment Charles continued to complain of the endless expense of keeping up the estate. He moved his family to the Circus, and Summerhill was left unoccupied, but he could neither sell nor let it. In 1826 he decided, therefore, to dispose of the house in the Circus and move back to Summerhill. "Dispose", once again, is vague, and one is left not knowing whether 27 Circus was owned or rented. He rented two rooms in 23 Gay Street for his practice. In 1828 he was forced to sell some ground rents, but does not state which – possibly both Sion Place and Camden Crescent. Edward Parry had also inherited a small interest in the estate. According to Ann Parry,[3] when he wrote to his intended father-in-law, Sir John Stanley, in 1826 declaring his intentions, he also told Sir John about his income – his salary as Hydrographer was £600 a year, Captain's half pay £191, and £231 from other sources including the title to four houses in Sion Place. The ground rent on the houses was £8 per house per annum, and, as noted earlier, it was divided among three people. Presumably Edward's rents were not included in the sale.

Charles continued to occupy Summerhill and 23 Gay Street until 1841. In 1842 his address appears in the *Directory* as Summerhill only. By 1845, Charles, then in his sixties, decided to leave Summerhill and, because he had still been unable to sell it, decided to sell the contents and let the house unfurnished. Edward wrote to sympathise with this necessary move. In 1845 Charles offered the contents of the library to the United Hospital (see Library). He also donated part of the fossil collection to the Bath Royal Literary and Scientific Institution but there is no trace of the bulk of the collection, and it may have been included in the sale of contents of the house. He may also have included part of the library in the sale (see Library). The *Bath Directory* still classified him as a physician in 1846 and 1848, but his address was given as Elmhurst, Batheaston, where he was living temporarily with the Bedfords, his wife's family. He retired to Brighton in 1849, and died there in 1860, aged eighty-one. He was buried in All Saints Church, Weston, Bath where there is a memorial tablet, on which he is described as "of Summerhill". Whether that should be interpreted to mean that he still owned the house is uncertain. No record of its sale has been found.

Among later owners, those in occupation for the longest period were the Blaines. Robert Stickney Blaine, later Sir Robert, was Mayor of Bath in 1872. The City Archives have an undated photograph of the house when owned by Sir Robert Blaine. The house was burned down in 1912. Some remnants of the house remain, a crumbling balustrade in the garden of No 1 Sion Hill Place, now also called Summerhill to add to the confusion.

Sir Sydney comments that "we have hardly anything left of my great-grandfather's furniture, pictures, and miscellaneous collections".

Dr Parry's Bust

According to Sir Sydney Parry,[4] not long before Caleb's death in March 1822, Lucius Gahagan made a life mask of him. Sir Sydney describes it as follows . . . "The process of making such masks was so irksome that they never gave a satisfactory result." And later . . . "The head was covered with plaster of Paris with straws inserted to breathe through."[5] It seems unlikely that a dying man would have been put through that ordeal, and it may well have been a death mask. Parry died on 9 March and the funeral was about a week later. This would have given time for a mask to be made. The bust does not suggest a man of sixty-six paralysed and dying but rather a handsome, robust, healthy man in his prime.

Lucius Gahagan settled in Bath about 1820. In 1824 he made two statues, "Commerce" and "Genius", for the facade of 9 Quiet Street, and in 1831 he made a head of Garrick for the Garrick Head Hotel. The author of his short biography also mentions the bust of Parry among Gahagan's works.[6] Monkland says of Gahagan's work "some of his casts are of a very superior description, and his modelled busts and statuettes are, for the most part, speaking likenesses".[7]

Two copies of the bust were made. One went to each of Caleb's sons, Dr Charles Henry Parry and Admiral Sir Edward Parry. The bust that went to Admiral Parry remained in the family until 1926.

In 1925 a plaque was placed over the door at 25 Circus and Sir Sydney Parry was invited to the unveiling but was unable to attend. In 1926 he wrote to the Bath Corporation thanking them for commemorating his grandfather, Sir W. Edward Parry, the Arctic navigator, and his great-grandfather Dr Caleb Hillier Parry, and regretted that he had been unable to be present at the ceremony. He offered the Corporation three life size busts, one from the life mask of Dr C.H. Parry, one from a life mask of Admiral Sir W. Edward Parry, and a cast from the bust of Sir Benjamin Hobhouse, Dr Parry's brother-in-law. He was retiring from the Deputy Chairmanship of Customs and Excise, and was moving from London to a small house in Sussex. He hoped to find a permanent home for the busts in the city with which they were connected.[8] They were accepted by the Victoria Art Gallery.

Before the last war the Victoria Art Gallery occasionally lent sculptures to the Bath School of Art for students to draw, and these three busts were among those lent. The school had a chequered history. For some time it was in the old Technical College in Beau Street. In 1938 Clifford Ellis, from the Academy of Art at Corsham, became headmaster, and pressed for independent status for the Art School. This was granted, and it moved from the Technical College into three adjoining houses in Green Park. A large part of Green Park, including the Art School, was destroyed in the bombing raids in 1942, and the busts were lost along with everything else.[9]

The second bust went to Charles Parry. After he left Summerhill in 1846 he may have taken it with him to Brighton. However, in 1857 he donated it to the Bath Royal Literary and Scientific Institution, then still in its original building in Terrace Walk. In 1932, when the building was demolished as part of a road widening scheme, the B.R.L.S.I. moved into 18 Queen Square. In 1939, at the beginning of the last war, the contents were packed and moved to Bristol Museum for safety. Fortunately they escaped damage during the many air raids on Bristol. After the war, they were returned to Bath, but there is no record of the Parry bust, which seems to have disappeared. In 1960 the Reference Library moved into 18 Queen Square, where it remained until 1990/91 when it moved to the new library at the Podium.

After the library moved out, a temporary curator was appointed to check the museum collection. He was asked by the author to keep a look-out for any items attributable to Caleb or Charles Parry, but found none. However he found the missing bust of Caleb Parry under the basement stairs, behind a pile of cleaning material.[10] It was dirty but in reasonably good condition, probably as a result of being pushed under the stairs and forgotten. It is engraved on the back of the pedestal:– "Caleb Hillier Parry MD FRS L Gahagan fecit, April 1st 1822 published as the Act directs". There is also a label which was attached to the bust which states,

Dr Caleb Hiller Parry
(Father of Captain Parry (Arctic Explorer) later Admiral)
Important as this is the only image of C.H.P.
History of Medicine in Bath
Don. 1857 Parry.

Charles Henry Parry (1779–1860)

Dr Parry decided at a very early stage that his first son, Charles, should become a doctor and join him in practice in Bath. Much thought and money were devoted to Charles Parry's education and he received the best teaching available in Bath. Caleb Parry often took the young boy with him when making country visits, but he failed to arouse any real enthusiasm in Charles for a medical career. In his autobiography, no semblance of modesty has prevented Charles from listing his accomplishments, in all of which he claims to have excelled, many European languages – modern and ancient, dancing, drawing, painting, fencing etc.[11]

In 1795 he was sent to a school in Greenwich, London, to study, and to meet the best company. Later he was sent abroad to Gottingen where he became friendly with Professor Blumenbach and his son. While there he translated a treatise on fevers by Gottfried Reich, to which his father added an appendix.[12] Charles attended lectures in Natural History, Physiology and Chemistry but also found time for long holidays and travel.

While abroad he became friendly with Samuel Taylor Coleridge and in May 1799 made a walking tour of the Harz Mountains with him. The party was completed by his younger brother Frederick, and by Clement Carlyon whose book[13] dedicated to Charles Parry contains details of this tour. The tour was also described in detail by Coleridge in letters to his wife Sara. Describing a rural musical incident he writes "I am no judge of music – it pleased me! and Mr Parry who plays himself, assured me it was uncommonly good".[14]

Charles Parry's friendship with Coleridge led to association with Southey and Wordsworth. In 1839 Wordsworth came to Bath and spent many agreeable days with Charles at Summerhill; and an exchange of letters is preserved in the Bodleian Library.[15]

Charles was not keen to qualify or to practice medicine, "a servile pursuit", "an occupation creating bustle and confusion eminently interfered with all that domestic comfort . . . without which all the wealth of the world is unprofitably acquired" and so on. In 1796 he came home to Sion Hill for a short time.

In 1801 he returned to Bath via Yarmouth, and notes that he had made little progress in that which was to be his permanent destiny. His estimate of the profession, he says, was unfavourable, its position in society unsatisfactory, and he strongly disliked the idea of being subjected to the whims of patients. However he was persuaded to go to Edinburgh to complete his medical studies. He graduated in 1804 with a thesis on Synocho Tropica or continuous fever. In 1806 he passed the examinations of the College of Physicians in London. In spite of his father's wishes he decided not to come to Bath, but instead, in 1807, he settled in Cheltenham to practise the "servile profession" and to be admitted to society "on tolerance of the higher classes".

Jenner, now an established physician in Cheltenham, was kind to young Charles whom he treated like a son. Charles records that, when his wife was ill in 1813, Jenner looked after her, and spent a week with them. Charles Parry also attended several meetings at Jenner's house and was a strong supporter of vaccination, and an active member of many committees.

In 1822 Jenner wrote and published a short work entitled *A letter to Charles Henry Parry MD FRS etc etc on the Influence of Artificial Eruptions. . .*[16] In 1820 Mr Bedford (Charles's father-in-law or brother-in-law?) decided to settle in Bath, and bought a property in Batheaston, originally part of Cold Bath Farm, to the west of the Fosse Way. He built a large house there and called it Elmhurst. The handsome house is still there in Old Fosse Lane, but the name was changed to Eden Park by Sir Edwin Leather MP. In 1822 Jenner's only daughter Catherine married John Yeend Bedford of Southbank, Edgbaston, near Birmingham thus relating Charles Parry and Edward Jenner by marriage. This may explain why Jenner stayed at Elmhurst, not Summerhill, when he visited Caleb Parry a few months before the latter's death.[17]

In 1810, although worried about his father's deteriorating health, Charles resisted all Caleb's attempts to persuade him to join his practice in Bath. He reports that he managed to defer the move until 1815 after "a long and most uncomfortable correspondence with my dear father on his proposal that we should leave Cheltenham and settle at Bath".

After Caleb's stroke Charles took over his fathers practice. He was elected to the staff of the General Hospital in 1818 and succeeded his father at the Casualty Hospital and the Puerperal Charity. He says that he held these appointments for seven years, but the records of the General Hospital show him as being on the staff from 1818–22.[18] Charles says that he gave up these appointments in 1826 when the United Hospital was being formed. He was offered the position of Senior Physician but "on a large view of the case, a consideration of its unprofitableness, and the great devotion of time which it required", he declined the offer.

In 1825 a chapter in Britton's *Account of Bath Abbey* was devoted to Dr Caleb Parry, and in 1830 the definitive biography appeared in William Macmichael's *Lives of British Physicians*. Both were unsigned but in his autobiography Charles acknowledged writing them.

His wife gave birth to seven daughters, one of whom died in infancy. Thus Charles had no sons to carry on the name of Parry.

Frederick George (1783–1804)

Caleb Parry's second son was also given the best education available, and later he joined his brother Charles abroad, where he was to study languages and commerce. He formed one of the walking party with his brother, Clement Carlyon and Coleridge. The latter wrote an amusing couplet about him.

> We walked – the younger Parry bore our goods
> Over d-d bad roads, through d-d delightful woods.

Frederick Parry was the youngest in the party. He suffered from asthma, and as he was not always able to keep up with the others, he was allowed to ride a pony. He showed his true British patriotism when he wrote "as the Brocken majestically towers over the surrounding hills, so does England, the queen of isles, soar above the other nations of the earth". In the evenings they entertained themselves by singing songs and ditties, a favourite being "Sally of our Alley".

Frederick went to Frankfurt where he remained until 1802, but he had to return to England as he had become seriously ill. He was diagnosed as suffering from hydrocephalus and died soon after returning, much to the distress of his parents.

William Edward Parry (1790–1855)

It was through the youngest son William Edward Parry that the family has descended to the present day. Edward did not have the special tuition and foreign travel that his two older brothers had enjoyed. At the age of thirteen he left home to join the Navy. His distinguished career has been fully described by Miss Ann Parry and at an earlier date by Rev Edward Parry.[19]

His Naval career, starting in 1803 meant that he was away from home most of the time, and was hardly an active participant in the family life. In 1808 he spent his Christmas leave with the family in Bath. In 1817 he was recalled from Bermuda "in consequence of a severe family affliction. His father, in the preceding October, had been seized with a paralytic attack which deprived him of the use of his right side and reduced him, for the remaining six years of his life, to a state of great suffering and helplessness".[20]

While in Bath he helped with his parents' move to 7 Sion Place. It was in this year that he applied to join the expedition to the Arctic under Captain Ross. While in London, sorting out the details of the expedition, he lived with his uncle Sir Benjamin Hobhouse. A few months later, when his ship was off Lowestoft, he was visited by his other uncle Dr Edward Rigby.

In 1820 he returned to Bath after his first voyage in Hecla, and was given the freedom of the City of Bath, and a valuable piece of plate. According to Charles, their father was well enough to derive great pleasure from the visit. Caleb was able to read and correct Edward's manuscript using his left hand. In 1821 Edward was elected FRS. His father Caleb and his brother Charles had already become Fellows, so that all three male member of the Parry family were Fellows of the Royal Society at the same time. The Bath and West Society presented him with the Bedfordian Gold Medal, an honour already conferred on his father in 1817. He was at sea in 1822, when Caleb died, and it was not until 1823, on returning from his second voyage, that he found letters waiting for him telling him of his father's death. The many geographical features, bays, capes etc., around the cost of Greenland and Canada, which have been named after him, remain as a permanent monument to his great Arctic explorations.

Dr Parry's Daughters

Of the daughters, Maria (1781–1849) married Rev. Thomas Garnier, who later became Dean of Winchester. Sarah Matilda (Matty) (1782–1852) and Gertrude Trevor (Gatty) (1788–1848), being unmarried, remained at home and helped their mother look after their paralysed father during his final years. They managed to interpret his imperfect speech and wrote down his reminiscences which he dictated to them, and which have been deposited in the Scott Polar Research Institute, Cambridge. After his death they remained with their mother. When they left 7 Sion Hill, they stayed for a time with Charles at Summerhill, and in 1828 they moved with Sarah to 76 Baker Street, London. After Sarah's death they went to live with their youngest sister Caroline (1792–1859) who had married Joseph Martineau. Elizabeth Emma (1789–1818) married Sir John Eardley Wilmot whose son edited and published Charles Parry's book on his grandfather, Joshua Parry.

Later Generations

The Parry family has continued to produce distinguished members. The Rt. Rev. Edward Parry (1830–90), the eldest surviving son of Admiral Sir Edward Parry, entered the church where he had a distinguished career. He was closely associated with Dr Tait, his old headmaster at Rugby, who became Archbishop of Canterbury. Rev Edward Parry followed him to Canterbury as Archdeacon and in 1870 "he was consecrated Bishop Suffragan of Dover". He died in 1890 aged 60. "He was buried in St Martin's Churchyard, Canterbury – not within the magnificent tomb in Canterbury Cathedral, surmounted by his recumbent effigy . . . Incidently this was the last "tomb" to be allowed in the cathedral . . . The Parry memorial library of the Kings School, Canterbury, was set up about the same time".[21]

Rev. E Parry's eldest son Edward Archibald Parry (1860–1943) also chose the Church, and eventually became Bishop of Guiana, and Archbishop of the West Indies. He remained unmarried.

His younger brother, Sir F. Sydney Parry, CB KBE (1861–1941) was the second son of Rev. Edward Parry. It is from him that the present line is descended. He entered the Civil Service in 1885 and, after a distinguished career, he was appointed Deputy Chairman of Customs and Excise. After he retired he worked on the family papers and wrote a short Parry Family History for his descendants.

In 1922 he was invited to the "unveiling of the Mural Tablet to Admiral Sir Edward Parry at 27 The Circus, Bath by Sir Martin Conway MP", but was unable to attend. In 1925, when Edward Parry's father was belatedly remembered, and the tablet was replaced by the present one, honouring Dr Caleb Parry as well as his son, he was again invited but was again unable to attend.

A third brother, Admiral Sir John Franklin Parry (1863–1926) became Hydrographer of the Navy (as his grandfather had been before him) and established the International Hydrographic Bureau at Monte Carlo at the invitation of Prince Albert of Monaco.

Sir Sydney Parry's only son, Admiral Sir (William) Edward Parry (1893–1972) had a distinguished naval career. He was Captain of the cruiser *Achilles* at the battle of the River Plate (13 December 1939), Captain of the battle cruiser *Renown* which carried Churchill across the Atlantic to meet Roosevelt, Director of Naval Intelligence (1946–48), and Commander-in-Chief of the Indian Navy (1948–51). His only son, Peter Edward Parry (1923–83), after wartime service with the RNVR, became a Director of P & O and Chairman of the passenger branch of the company.[22]

Thus, a distinguished family whose members have made outstanding contributions to medicine, exploration, the Navy and the Church is still continuing 400 years after its records began.

PART TWO

Research and Publications

CHAPTER 7

Publications at 13 Catharine Place

The Rhubarb Saga

Parry's first medical publication appeared in the year 1786. A few years earlier Edmund Rack (1735–87) had settled in Bath. He was born in Norfolk to parents of humble means, and was apprenticed to a shopkeeper. However, he improved his position steadily, and by 1775 he had acquired sufficient means to retire to Bath, where he wrote and published several works. He was especially interested in agriculture. Although he had no practical experience of farming, he understood the value and importance of agriculture as a source of national wealth. He wrote several articles in the *Farmer's Magazine* suggesting the formation of a society, based in Bath, to promote interest in agriculture, and to provide up-to-date information.

His was the driving force that led to the formation of just such a society. On 8 May 1777, twenty-two people, mainly local doctors, clergymen and lawyers met and formed "The Society instituted at Bath for the Encouragement of Agriculture, Arts, Manufactures, and Commerce in the Counties of Somerset, Wilts, Glocester, and Dorset, and the City and County of Bristol".[1] About thirteen years later the name was changed to the shorter "Bath and West of England Society for the encouragement of Agriculture, Arts, Manufactures, and Commerce."

The first book of Rules and Orders was published in 1777, but it was not until 1780 that the first volume of reports appeared under the title *Letters and Papers on Agriculture, Planting, etc. selected from the Correspondence-Book of the Society instituted at Bath etc.etc.* The first volume of reports contains an undated article entitled "On the Mode of Cultivating and Curing the Rheum Palmatum or true Rhubarb. (Communicated by a Gentleman at Minehead)".[2] More than thirty letters and articles on this subject appeared in the next few years.

The use of rhubarb in medicine has a long history going back to antiquity and, unlike many ancient remedies, its use has continued to the present day. In the 1934 edition of the *London Hospital*

Pharmacopoeia, which listed the medicines and drugs available from the Hospital Dispensary, there were ten mixtures containing Rhubarb; and the 1989 *Martindale* still lists no less than five laxative mixtures based on Rhubarb. The medicinal drug is derived from the dried underground roots of the Rheum Palmatum or its hybrids. Roots are obtained from China, England, India etc. Various chemical criteria are laid down.

The "Gentleman from Minehead" pointed out that rhubarb was a most useful medicine, but it was a most expensive import from Turkey and Russia. He suggested that the Society should offer a prize to the person "who shall raise the greatest quantity of the best kind". It was no surprise to read that he had already started with some vigorous plants in his garden which grew 8 feet high. The roots weighed 8–12 lbs each and, when cured, he believed the product was as good as the imported Turkish rhubarb. He sent some of the cured root to the Society for the doctors in Bath to test, and also some seeds for anyone who wished to cultivate it. The letter continued with details of how he had grown the plants, the best time to lift the roots, and how to cure them. This letter was followed by extensive correspondence from various people around the country including some well known London physicians – John Fothergill and John Coakley Lettsom. Following a letter in December 1778 from a "Gentleman near Norwich", the committee decided that it would be helpful to obtain a medical opinion on the specimens being sent in by readers. They asked Dr William Falconer, physician to the General Hospital (now the Royal National Hospital for Rheumatic Diseases) to examine the specimens of English rhubarb.

Dr Falconer's report[3] gives a clear picture of the chemical and pharmacological investigations that could be undertaken at that time. His paper commenced with an erudite historical review, through the Roman period of Celsus and Paulus Aeginata, to Linnaeus, to which was added a discussion of exactly what these authors were referring to. He went on to discuss the desirable qualities of the root and the powder. He compared the specimens received with Turkish Rhubarb for the following qualities: appearance when cut and when powdered, specific gravity, appearance of a tincture made with brandy, and an infusion with water. He also tried it on several patients, and decided that its operation was "such as might be expected from the best foreign rhubarb".

After this report the committee felt that there was a need for further investigation. In 1780 they decided to offer three prizes. The first being fifty pounds "To the person who, in the spring of 1780, shall sow and duly cultivate, and in the autumn of 1784 produce . . . not less than one hundred pounds of rhubarb". The second and third prizes were smaller amounts of money for smaller weights of rhubarb.[4]

Though correspondence continued little else could happen before the autumn of 1784, when it was expected that specimens would be submitted and sent to selected doctors for assessment. The greater number of the samples seems to have been given to Dr William Falconer, who enlisted the help of young Dr Parry who had been in Bath for five years and was on the staff of the Pauper Charity. Some rhubarb was also given to Dr A. Fothergill (not John Fothergill 1712–1780).

The reports appeared in 1786.[5–11] Falconer's first paper is an expansion of his original report with some new tests. One consisted of making solutions of different powders in water, spirits and brandy. Strips of cardboard were dipped into each, allowed to dry, and the colours compared. It is not clear what he expected to learn from this early attempt at colorimetry. The next paper reports "Experiments with Rhubarb No I and No II, made at the General Hospital, by Mr Farnell, the Apothecary; a very sensible, accurate, and well informed Person". He reported, briefly, tweenty-nine case histories e.g. "Case VII John Way, aged sixty, afflicted with rheumatic pains and trembling in his hands, took half a drachm of No II. It operated four times in eight hours, and without griping". Patients in the trial were given only one of the extracts that were being tested, and in no case was the Turkey rhubarb given. Dr Falconer concluded that, if properly prepared, English rhubarb could be as good as imported roots. Dr Fothergill gave all three preparations to four patients and came to the same conclusion.

Parry's conclusions were in line with those of his colleagues, but his approach to the problem, his method of investigating it, and his presentation of his case reports are all strikingly different. The paper is important, not for what it says about rhubarb, but for what it says about Parry. He understood – it is not clear that the others did – that this was a comparative trial and his first group of cases is headed "Comparative Effects of the three Kinds". He realised that to compare three samples, each patient had to receive all three, and the results for each had to be recorded separately for each patient. In each case the results were presented in tabular form. The first group of ten patients received doses of all three samples. Furthermore, whether by chance or by intention, the order in which the samples were administered varied randomly.

A further eleven patients were also tested but as they were not given all three specimens, the results are recorded separately.

Clearly, here we have a doctor who already recognised the basic principles of a comparative clinical trial, and also the importance of accurate recording.

Carotid Compression

By the latter part of the eighteenth century as a result of the increasing number of descriptions of pathological findings, especially the publications of Morgagni, doctors had given up the humoral and other general theories. But they were still seeking explanations for those diseases where careful post mortem dissections failed to reveal any obvious naked-eye pathology. There was little real progress until the latter part of the nineteenth century with the development of bacteriology, cellular pathology and all that followed.

At an early stage of his career Parry developed the theory that many otherwise unexplained diseases, where there was no obvious gross pathology, were due to "determination of the blood". The *Oxford English Dictionary* gives its eighteenth-century use as a "tendency of flow of the blood to a particular part". Parry believed that the concept of excessive determination of the blood was especially useful in explaining diseases of the nervous system,[12] and the theory reappears later as an explanation for many diseases in his book, *The Elements of Pathology and Therapeutics*.[13] Parry first suggested the theory in a paper read in January 1789 to the Medical Society of London, which was published in 1792.[14] The paper had a long title – "On the Effects of Compression of the Arteries in various Diseases, and particularly in those of the Head; with Hints towards a new Mode of treating Nervous Disorders". He also read the paper at a meeting of the Fleece Society on 13 June 1792. On 20 December 1810 he read a short supplementary paper on the same subject at the Royal Society, which was published in 1811.[15] No account has been found of immediate reactions to the original paper, but it was criticised later. Although the whole concept was wrong, its application lead him to observe and record for the first time several interesting conditions.

Parry did not take kindly to criticism, and it is amusing to read in some of his medical and agricultural works, the fighting style with which he answered his critics. Here is a short sample taken from the start of a long letter to the editor of the *Monthly Magazine* in answer to the criticism of his paper on Arterial Compression which appeared in *The Anatomy of the Human Body* by Mr John Bell, surgeon, of Edinburgh.

> To the Editor of the Monthly Magazine (May 1798)
> Sir
>
> It was not till yesterday, that I happened to see a work intituled, "The Anatomy of the Human Body", by Mr John Bell, surgeon, of Edinburgh. This work contains excellent engravings, and much useful anatomical information; but is debased by a stile of the most dogmatical assertion, by a puerile affectation of pleasantry, by frequent misconception and misrepresentation of the opinions of others, and by the most scurrilous abuse of all living authors. I have had the misfortune to be plentifully splashed by this writer, in his headlong plunge into the foul sink of obloquy.[16]

Medical theory and understanding have changed so radically since Caleb Hillier Parry's day, that it is pointless to discuss this theory at length. It was not accepted generally. However, from this theory it followed that if the cause of a disease or symptom was excessive blood flow to an organ or region, the logical treatment was to reduce the blood flow.

The greater part of this paper[17] deals with the symptoms of a grossly hysterical young woman. She had attacks of "a state which the attendants called fainting" during which her "spasm and convulsions very suddenly ceased, and all the senses, except sometimes that of hearing, were also suspended. But no coldness came on the extremities, the face retained its colour". Parry notes ruefully that "she had never any recollection of any thing which had passed during the paroxysm, though it was always accompanied with that sort of consistency, both of reasoning and conduct, which seemed particularly well calculated to attain the end proposed". Her main symptoms, however, were attacks of "convulsive contractions of the sterno-mastoid and recti abdominis muscles; in consequence of which the head and body were bent forward with a force which could not be overcome". These symptoms suggest that she had hyperventilation producing the spasms of tetany – severe spasms of the sterno-mastoid muscles, contracture of the abdominal muscles producing emprosthotonos, associated with orthopnoea. Tetany in children was described by Clarke in 1815. Parry's case may be the first description of tetany due to hyperventilation.

After a year during which he tried every drug or mixture available,

Parry decided that her troubles must be due to excessive determination of the blood to the brain, and he attempted to reduce the flow by compressing the carotid arteries. He found that compression of one artery was enough to stop the patient's fits or convulsions, but the effect was only temporary and the symptoms recurred as soon as the pressure was released.

Another symptom which Parry noted was the occurrence of severe headaches associated with heat and flushing of the head and neck. Her "fits of delirium were preceded by a sense of fulness and throbbing pain in the head, accompanied with a great degree of heat and flushing about the head and neck". Kelly[18] believes this is the first description of histamine cephalgia.

Parry was pleased with the effect of coronary pressure in his patient and proceeded to try it in other cases.

A patient who came to see him was suffering from epileptic fits "When they are of any length, they are accompanied with convulsive twitchings of the right arm and leg, and the right side of the face. While he was speaking I observed an appearance about his face as though a paroxysm was approaching. His eyes began to assume a vacant stare, and convulsions were coming on about the throat. Under the usual pretence of feeling the pulse in the neck, I immediately made a strong compression of the right carotid artery. The convulsions ceased". The patient was shown how to compress the carotid artery and was able to control his fits.

Another original observation made by Parry was the value of carotid compression in cases of hemicrania. "It nearly or totally removes the hemicrania of the side on which the compression is made". Sir Thomas Lewis[19] comments that this is "the first notice of the relief of pain given by carotid compression in hemicrania, a fact rediscovered in recent times".

Parry's most important observation on the use of carotid compression is reported in his book on angina[20] "In patients, whose hearts have been beating with undue quickness and force, I have often, in a few seconds, retarded their motion many pulsations in a minute, by strong pressure on one of the carotid arteries. An instance of this kind occurred in the case of the late Admiral K. S****, who laboured under a hemiplegia, succeeding violent apoplexy. His pulse was quick, and already very full and tense. Pressure on one carotid almost instantly reduced the pulse fifteen or twenty beats in a minute, without having previously increased either its frequency or strength; and the pulse returned to its former state as soon as the pressure was removed". Parry repeated this several times in the presence of his colleagues Dr Fraser and Dr Ewart who "were witnesses of this fact, which was repeated more than once with the same effect".

Sir Thomas Lewis[21] discusses the modern interest in the carotid sinus and its powerful controlling influence on the heart rate. After referring to the work of Waller, Czermak, and Hering, he points out that the phenomenon was first observed and recorded by Caleb Parry many years earlier.

Parry was a remarkably accurate observer. In the two medical publications produced while living at Catharine Place he made a series of original observations. In the paper on Arterial Compression he gave what is probably the first account of tetany due to hyperventilation, and the first description of histamine cephalgia. He was the first to record the effect of carotid compression in relieving the pain of hemicrania, and its effect in preventing attacks of Jacksonian epilepsy. In his book on Syncope Anginosa, in addition to recognising the role of coronary circulation insufficiency, he demonstrated that pressure on the carotid artery could slow the pulse.

Syncope Anginosa

The history of angina pectoris is well documented and there are many books and articles on the subject, of which only a few have been consulted. The object of these notes is to highlight Parry's important contribution to the elucidation of the cause. In order to put his work in context it will be necessary to repeat some well known historical facts.

On 30 June 1788, Parry, who had been elected President, took the chair at the first meeting of the Fleece Medical Society. He read an introductory address, "and also a case and dissection of the Angina Pectoris or Syncope Anginosa: together with a disquisition on the Symptoms, Pathology, prevention and cure of that disorder".[22] The text was not recorded in the minutes, but it forms the substance of the second chapter of Parry's book on Angina.[23] This was the first book to be devoted entirely to the discussion of angina, and was soon translated into French (1806). In the introduction he writes:

> More than thirty years have now elapsed since Dr. Heberden published a description of a disease highly alarming as to its consequences, and till then, as it should seem, unnoticed among physicians . . . The pathology has hitherto remained in a state so uncertain, as to have suggested no probable means of cure or

> relief. These circumstances have induced me to attempt an enquiry into the nature and causes of the Angina Pectoris, as they are deducible from the actual symptoms, and from dissections.

There had been many accounts in the early literature, mostly of single case reports of patients with symptoms of chest pain suggesting angina, and other reports of post-mortem findings of softening or rupture of the heart muscle, probably due to infarction.[24] Parry reviewed all that were available to him.

In 1768 Dr William Heberden read his paper to the Royal College of Physicians, and it appeared in print in 1772.[25] Heberden was the first to recognise that there was a clearly defined clinical syndrome, and in his classical description he described all the main features especially the chest pain. He recognised the progressive nature of the disease and the poor prognosis. Although he saw about a hundred cases, in none of the fatal ones was a post-mortem done, and he had no idea of the cause. He gave it the name 'Angina Pectoris' and attributed it to a "spasmodic disorder".

In the same year that his paper appeared, 1772, an account in English was published in the *Critical Review*.[26, 27] It was read by a sufferer, who offered his body for dissection. He died soon after, and John Hunter was asked to perform the dissection. Edward Jenner was present, and said later that the coronary arteries had not been examined.[28] The identity of the patient signing himself "unknown" remains thus. In some accounts he is referred to as Dr Anonymous but there is no reason to suppose that he was a doctor. Heberden's paper stimulated a search for the explanation of angina. Dr John Fothergill reported a patient, who died in 1773 and was also examined by Hunter, who found that the coronaries had become one piece of bone. But no conclusion as to cause was deduced from his finding.

Jenner was the first to suggest a direct connection between angina and coronary artery disease, malorganization of the coronary arteries, as he called it.[29] It was through Parry's book[30] that Jenner's work became known. His observations were made before 1788, when Parry read his paper to the Fleece which was intended to add to Jenner's cases and confirm his opinion about malorganization of the coronaries. Jenner had already discussed his views with his friends, and this was probably before 1785, when Hunter made his last visit to Bath and was looked after by the twenty-nine year old Parry. "With these observations of Dr Jenner we were well acquainted in the

Society. Many of them were indeed communicated to us as they arose".[31]

It is interesting to speculate on the reasons for Jenner not publishing his findings. Baron[32] found a letter in Jenner's papers addressed to Heberden in which he speculated that Hunter's angina attacks were due to coronary artery disease. The letter probably was not sent. There is no evidence that Jenner regularly kept copies of his letters, hence the one sided correspondence with John Hunter. Jenner excused himself:[33]

> At this very time, my valued friend, Mr. John Hunter, began to have the symptoms of Angina Pectoris too strongly marked upon him; and this circumstance prevented any publication of my ideas on the subject, as it must have brought on an unpleasant conference between Mr Hunter and me. I mentioned both to Mr Cline and Mr Home, my notions of the matter, at one of Mr Hunter's Sunday night meetings; but they did not seem to think much of them. When, however, Mr Hunter died, Mr Home very candidly wrote to me, immediately after the dissection, to tell me I was right.

Hunter died in 1793, after which time the original reluctance to publish was no longer valid, and Jenner might well have reported his case and that of Dr Paytherus. He still had plenty of time. He had not yet published his short work on vaccination nor was he involved in the controversy and correspondence that ensued. The explanation probably lies in Jenner's reluctance to put pen to paper. Dr John Fosbroke, who was his assistant in Cheltenham and for years helped with his correspondence, knew him as intimately as anyone. In his fulsome eulogy of Jenner[34] he describes him as a great procrastinator. ". . . Seated to execute something half finished, now applying to, now receding from his task . . . the postponement of any requisite undertaking till it could no longer be postponed . . ." etc.

But why did Parry not publish his 1788 address to the Fleece Medical Society? Unlike Jenner he was a facile writer, and a tireless worker, and it would have been in character for him to have published all three cases. He excuses himself in the introduction to his book.[35]

> During their course (Jenner's observation) I witnessed the remarkable case of the Rev. Mr S***, whose body after death exhibited appearances so coincident with those which from the symptoms I had expected, and relying on the accuracy of Dr Jenner, had predicted, that I was induced to relate it to the society, with a variety of pathological remarks intended to illustrate Dr Jenner's position, that the Angina Pectoris was a disease of the heart, connected with mal-organization of the

> coronary arteries. This dissertation was read to the society in the month of July 1788. As it appeared to me to throw some light on this disease, I always intended it for publication; but much professional occupation followed, and prevented the accomplishment of my purpose.

The introduction to Parry's book published in 1799, recognises Jenner's claim to being the first to suggest that angina was connected with "malorganization" of the coronary arteries, and Parry gives him full credit.

> And it was suggested by Dr Jenner, that the Angina Pectoris arose from some morbid change in the structure of the heart, which change was probably ossification, or some similar disease, of the coronary arteries. To some questions which I have lately put to the excellent pathologist, as to the series of observations which produced that opinion, I have received the following answer: "The first case I ever saw of Angina Pectoris, was that in the year 1772, published by Dr Heberden, with Mr Hunter's dissection. There, I can almost positively say, the coronary arteries of the heart were not examined. Another case of a Mr Carter, at Dursley, fell under my care. In that, after having examined the more important parts of the heart, without finding anything by means of which I could account either for his sudden death, or the symptoms preceding , I was making a transverse section of the heart pretty near its base, when my knife struck against something so hard and gritty, as to notch it. I well remember looking up to the ceiling, which was old and crumbling, conceiving that some plaster had fallen down. But on further scrutiny the real cause appeared: the coronaries were become bony canals. Then I began a little to suspect.
>
> Soon afterwards Mr Paytherus met with a case. Previously to our examination of the body, I offered him a wager that we should find the coronary arteries ossified. This, however, proved not to be exactly true; but the coats of the arteries were hard, and a sort of cartilaginous canal was formed within the cavity of each artery, and there attached, so however as to be separable as easily as the finger from a tight glove. We then concluded that malorganization of these vessels was the cause of the disease."

Mr Paytherus provided Parry with a more detailed account of his case, which he published in full in the next chapter. Mr Bellamy, "frequently intemperate", had his first attack 12 August 1785 after an excess of port. The account of the attack suggests a small thrombosis. Less than a year later he developed angina of effort, and in due course died from an attack. The findings at the post-mortem, attended by Dr Hickes and Jenner, have already been noted in Jenner's letter.

Later, Parry's case, the third in the series, the Rev. Mr S . . ., was reported by him at the first meeting of the Fleece Medical Society. A full account is given in the book. The patient's symptoms suggest a severe coronary thrombosis, leading in a few days to his death. The body was opened thirty-three hours later by Messrs Atwood and Perry, surgeons. The gall bladder contained 2,654 distinct stones!

> The two coronary arteries were ossified in the substance of their coats in various portions, from their exit out of the aorta to the distance of four inches or more, in such a manner that the ossified parts were full three-fourths of that length, and a very small silver blow-pipe could not be made to pass within their cavity.

Parry's decision to write his book was the result of his second case, some time later. Mr M had a long history of various pains, including a little tightness across his chest. In 1796 he developed anginal pain while walking. Two more attacks followed in April 1797. A third attack was more serious. Parry was called to see him and his notes described a typical coronary thrombosis – severe pain, face and extremities pallid, cold sweat, and radial pulse difficult to feel. The patient's condition deteriorated steadily and he died a few hours later. Post-mortem by Mr Grant, in the presence of Drs Parry and Fraser, and Mr Mayhew, revealed a large heart buried in fat making it impossible to feel the coronary arteries. They were traced by dissection, and both were found to contain hard bony tubes "and had a perforation not large enough to receive the smallest probe."

In the third chapter Parry reviewed the older literature that was available to him. He believed that of the three cases described by Morgagni only one was a true case of angina, but, although the patient came to post-mortem, no lesion of the coronary arteries was noted. After giving a brief summary of the usual symptoms, with many quotations from older authors, he discussed the most recent cases described by Heberden, Fothergill, Wall and others.

There was an important contribution by Dr Black of Newry between Parry's Fleece paper of 1788 and the publication of his book in 1799. Parry was aware of "that excellently marked case and dissection by Dr Black" communicated in 1794 to the London Medical Society. He agreed that it was a genuine case of Angina Pectoris, found on dissection to have ossified coronary arteries, but pointed out that his paper to the Fleece antedates Black, while the cases of Jenner and Paytherus were even earlier. Dr Black's paper "had no share in producing the conclusion either of my friend Dr Jenner, or myself, as to the causes of the Angina Pectoris." He enlarges on this matter of priority later in the book.

One feature that Parry noted when he saw a patient during an attack was weakness of the pulse. Heberden, on the other hand, stated that he had not found the pulse to be disturbed during the paroxysm, and hence concluded that the heart was not affected. Parry was curious to know exactly what happened in a non-fatal attack of angina, and performed what may be the first exercise tolerance test on one of his patients.

> I have lately had a patient, long subject to attacks of a very pure Angina Pectoris, who permitted me to accompany him during a walk up hill, in order that I might be witness of what occurred during the fit. When the paroxysm was thus excited, I could perceive no symptom of disorder, in addition to the uneasiness in the breast, except a gradual and most evident diminution of the strength of the pulse; and I have no doubt that we shall invariably find the pulse become weaker in proportion to the violence of the paroxysm. This conclusion meets with abundant confirmation from the phaenomena attending the final paroxysms of the two last patients whose cases I have related above.

From these observations, weakening of the pulse or in his more severe cases almost impalpable pulse with profuse sweating, coldness and pallor of the face and extremities, Parry concluded that angina was a type of Syncope. Syncope, as used at that time, meant diminution of the motion of the heart, which if severe could be irrecoverable and lead to death. He called it Syncope Anginosa and after much discussion added it to the nosological table of Syncope put forward by his old teacher Dr Cullen.

In the next chapter Parry pointed out that at post-mortem the heart often "abounds in fat" and, as the coronary arteries are "nearly imbedded in a firm muscular substance", any abnormality in the arteries will not be discovered, unless a special effort is made to examine them. In his opinion any post-mortem report is unreliable unless this "special effort" has been made – ". . . no negative proof can in future be admitted, unless the examination be made in the manner which I have proposed."

Parry found it difficult to understand or account for the symptoms of angina on the basis of ossification of the coronaries alone. In some fatal cases of genuine angina no ossification had been found. Furthermore he pointed out the difficulty of believing "that a temporary disease should arise from permanent mal-conformation". He had already decided from his observations that angina was a form of syncope. He had also read "that Hoffman, who, as it would seem, was totally unacquainted with the phenomenon of ossified coronaries, lays it down as a principle, that one cause of Syncope is the want of a proper influx of good blood through vessels into the muscular substance of the heart".

This statement of a theoretical physiological principle combined with his observations of the actual facts, led to Parry's understanding of the mechanism. This is his great contribution to the angina saga.

He concluded, in a long tortuous statement that it was not the anatomical pathology of the coronaries that caused the symptoms, but the disturbance of function ie coronary circulatory insufficiency.

> The rigidity of the coronary arteries may act, proportionably to the extent of the ossification, as a mechanical impediment to the free motion of the heart; and though a quantity of blood may circulate through these arteries, sufficient to nourish the heart, as appears, in some instances, from the size and firmness of that organ, yet there may probably be less than what is requisite for ready and vigorous action. Hence, though a heart so diseased may be fit for the purposes of common circulation, during a state of bodily and mental tranquillity, and of health otherwise good, yet when any unusual exertion is required, its powers may fail, under the new and extraordinary demand. Accordingly we find, that paroxysms of the Syncope Anginosa are readily excited by those passions, the tendency of which is to stimulate the heart to excessive contraction.

This is generally accepted as the first recognition of the importance of coronary circulatory insufficiency in producing the symptoms and effects of angina pectoris.[36, 37]

Parry's observations and explanation were confirmed a few years later by Burns in Edinburgh.[38] Burns compared the effect of restricted coronary flow to the pain developing in a limb working with a ligature around it reducing its blood flow. The observations of Black, Jenner, Parry and Burns were overlooked for a hundred years or more, and attention was focussed on aortic disease as the cause, a notable advocate of that view being Sir Clifford Allbutt.[39, 40] Remarkably, the argument had already been anticipated by Parry in his book. Reviewing the literature he noted how often disease of the aorta (dilatation, induration or ossification) occurred, and recorded that it was present in six of the cases of angina to which he had referred. But aortic disease was not essential for the production of angina, as shown by the post-mortem findings in one case with a completely normal heart and aorta.

Parry also appreciated the fact that the reduced inadequate flow of blood would have an effect on the myocardium.

> As induration of the coronary arteries probably depends on causes which may alike operate on every other part of the heart and large vessels, there is no reason

why it may not be accompanied with any of those organic injuries which have been before described. And if we can suppose that the coronaries may be so obstructed as to intercept the blood, which should be the proper support of the muscular fibres of the heart, that organ must become thin and flaccid, and unequal to the task of circulation.

In the last part of the book there are two references to John Hunter, who was looked after by the young Parry when he made his fourth and last visit to Bath in 1785.

It is scarcely necessary to add, that the disease before us cannot be expected to exempt a patient from other complaints, totally unconnected with it. Thus Mr Hunter had many symptoms, which, probably, arose from an affection of the brain.

The symptoms are not described, and one is left wondering what cerebral symptoms Parry noted in Hunter in 1785, eight years before the latter's death. The second reference appears in the chapter dealing with treatment, which was largely a general regime.

It appears, however, from experience, that some gentle and long-continued stimuli have afforded considerable temporary relief in the Syncope Anginosa. This happened with regard to one of Dr Fothergill's patients from the Bath waters; and I observed the same effect in the case of Mr Hunter.

No other reference to Hunter has been found, but this is quite enough evidence to confirm that Parry looked after him on that visit.

It is in this book that Parry describes the effect of carotid compression in slowing the pulse.

To sum up, Jenner was the first to suggest a direct connection between the symptoms of angina and malorganization of the coronary arteries, and Parry realised that the circulatory inadequacy at times of need was the cause of the pain and diminished cardiac function.

Proudfit[41] says: "Though the term 'Heberden's syndrome' is appropriate, we might equally well speak of 'Jenner-Parry's disease'".

And finally Parry:

If the opinion be well founded, which I have endeavoured to support in the preceding pages, that the Syncope Anginosa is primarily owing to induration of the coronary arteries, we have no reason to expect that it will ever suffer a radical cure.

What would Parry say today!

CHAPTER 8

Publications at 27 Circus

Decay of Wood – Causes and Prevention

Every year the Bath and West Society published a volume of *Rules, Orders, and Premiums*. The list of prizes on offer came in many categories, and is a good indication of the current problems for which solutions were being sought. Among the premiums offered in 1804[1] was the following:– "3. Competition for preserving Wood – To the person who, in the year 1805, shall describe, to the satisfaction of this Society, a more cheap and durable composition than any now in common use, for covering and preserving from decay barn and other outside doors, weather boarding, gates, stiles, and other implements in husbandry: Three Guineas." The competition for preserving wood did not produce any contribution worthy of a prize that year. The first response appears to be a thirty-page essay by Dr Caleb Hillier Parry in 1807.[2] It was also in that same year he produced his prize essay on the production of fine wool, for the Board of Agriculture, which was published as a book.[3] There is no record of Parry having received a prize for his article on the decay of wood.

It has proved difficult to find any early research into the decay of wood, or a comprehensive review similar to that in Dr Parry's article, which attempts to deal with the problem systematically. The Science Museum Library in London was most helpful and provided some photocopies of early work on the problem.

The Index of Patents shows that on 9 December 1768 Humphrey Jackson took out a patent, No 910 on Preserving Timber.[4] His "Invention" was described as "The Method of Hardening, Toughening, or Rendering very Flexible and Preserving Wood and Timber in General from Speedy Rotting and Decay." His method consisted of boiling the wood for several hours in calcareous earth (i.e. containing lime or limestone) in water, then neutralising the solution by adding acid of vitriol (sulphuric acid) and boiling again.

The report on vitriol, in the section on Chemistry in the *Encyclopaedia Britannica*, 1797, contains the following note:[5] "In the retort, a fine red powder will remain, which is used in painting, and is called colcothar of vitriol. It is useful on account of its durability; and, when mixed with tar, has been employed as a preservative of wood from rotting; but Dr Lewis prefers finely powdered pit-coal. As a preservative for masts of ships, he recommends a mixture of tar and lamp black." And later "Solutions of green vitriol are also recommended for preserving wood, particularly the wheels of carriages, from decay. When all the pieces are fit for being joined together, they are directed to be boiled in a solution of vitriol for three or four hours. By this preparation wood becomes so hard, that moisture cannot penetrate it." This appears to be a forerunner of the modern method of tanalising wood.

The best contemporary account is in *Rees's Cyclopaedia* of 1819 in which the methods in current use are described under the separate headings of Hardening, Seasoning and Preserving.[6] The methods were those which had been used for many years. The Venetians, for example, who were famous for the soundness of their ships, prepared the timber by leaving it submerged in water for many years. The writer prefers creating a protective layer of charcoal on the outside by fire, i.e. charring the wood. Although he records the wide use of different paints, he condemns it, claiming that paint makes decay worse by sealing the moisture in the wood, and by concealing the damage that is occurring. The importance of ventilation is stressed. Many people preserve wood by smearing it with "oleaginous matter" e.g. linseed oil or tar. The Dutch used a coating of pitch and tar dusted with a coating of ground sea shells and sea sand. Others mix in coal dust or powdered charcoal. The advice is given that when a composite article is being preserved, e.g. a wheel, the component parts should be treated separately before the final product is assembled.

Parry's article starts by pointing out that once wood has been separated from its roots, i.e. killed, it "is subject to gradual destruction from two causes – rotting and the depredations of insects." Rot can occur in two ways, in the open air, or under cover i.e. dry rot. It is to the former that the premium refers, and he adds to the list of wooden structures likely to be affected – "posts, rails, water chutes (gutters and drains)." Parry notes some of the methods used to preserve recently killed animal tissue, e.g. freezing salmon in Scotland for conveyance to London, or the slow drying of thin strips of meat to produce "portable soup" (? pemmican). Slow drying of wood, as for that used in churches, can make it last for centuries; and wood buried in the earth or fully immersed in water will also resist decay. But in a post the part "which is just above or within the ground" decays rapidly. Parry called this "putrefactive fermentation" for which "the constant action of water aided by air" is needed. Where air and water can be excluded, rotting will not occur, as for example, the preservation of insects in amber.

First the cause, then the treatment. Parry goes on to discuss the "various expedients" that have been used, the most common being mixtures based on paint. The drying quality of paint was usually improved by boiling with metallic oxides, e.g. litharge (lead monoxide). This mixture had also been used successfully to paint onto umbrellas, or the silk of air balloons. Trials, Parry writes, had taken place in which dust or very fine sand had been added to the paint. He remembered having read "that charcoal buried in moist earth, had come down to us perfectly sound from the times of the Romans." He tried a method based on this to preserve some new water chutes. He oiled them thoroughly and, before they were dry, dredged them with powdered charcoal; after they were dry he painted the chutes with two coats of lead paint. Many years later the wood was still sound. Parry also had lasting results from a mixture described in 1783,[7] which he used on a fence and which was sound eighteen years later. The mixture also proved "efficacious in keeping iron from decay by rusting." After some observations on how to make the mixture he writes "This is all which occurs to me as to the mode of preserving wood when exposed to the weather."

Dry rot occurs under cover. After listing the indoor timbers likely to be affected, Parry notes that mould and fungi may grow on the wood, which have a recognisable odour. The process is similar to that which occurs outdoor – putrefactive fermentation "in connection with moisture without which . . . wood cannot putrefy." Indoors water is present as vapour in the air, and condenses on cold surfaces, thus causing a variety of problems such as peeling wallpaper, damp stonework, etc. Inner walls did not have the benefit of sun and wind to dry them, and whilst there may be sufficient movement of air to dry the visible surface of a wainscot, the surface next to the wall could remain wet.

There are several preventive measures which can be taken; put battens on the wall to make a false inner wall; making the wall thick so the cold cannot penetrate. Another possibility is to build a cavity wall, the solution recommended by Parry especially if the house is exposed on all sides. He forestalls the present fashion for insulation by suggesting that the cavity be filled with a non-conductor of heat, for example sifted coal ash or charcoal. [It would be interesting to know whether this was an original suggestion, and if not, how early insulated cavity walls were used.] He also recommends keeping all the rooms and staircases warm.

To avoid dry rot timber must be dried properly and for an adequate length of time. Building plans should allow for the passage of air along the surface of wood and all timber should be prepared before use by applying three or four coats of paint to make the surface impenetrable by water. The same mixture should be used as the one recommended for application outside.

Finally Parry refers briefly to the other cause of decay of wood, "the depredations of insects".

The article is a compendium of known methods of preservation of wood, with reports of some personal experiences. As it did not receive the prize it probably contains nothing original. It is impressive, however, that with all his other interests and activities, Parry was interested enough in wood preservation to make his own trials and experiments on his farm.

In 1817, the year after his stroke, another article on the decay of wood appeared in a collection of articles edited (?) by James Haviland.[8] The article "On the Decay of Wood and the Manner of Preventing it," is by C.H. Parry M.D. of Bath. The text appears to be a re-statement of the original paper with some additions. It could have been written by Caleb before his stroke or, more likely, by his son Charles.

Purpura

Anyone reading the medical writings and case notes of eighteenth-century doctors must be amazed at the failure to recognise the condition of anaemia. According to the *OED* the word did not come into use until 1836. Skinner[9] says that the word first appeared in English medical usage in 1829, but it was not until 1849 that it began to have a specific medical meaning. Indeed, diseases of the blood only started to be understood in the latter half of the nineteenth century, when the relevant laboratory techniques were developed. Parry usually made a point of examining, macroscopically, the blood of patients who had had venesection, after it had stood for some time. He recognised three layers, the solid red clot or crassamentum, a layer of what he called coagulated lymph, and the serum. He also appreciated that the proportions were constant, and in some of his case notes he records that the proportions were normal. Bleeding, usually by venesection, was a common therapeutic measure, and astonishing amounts of blood were withdrawn, one might almost say "with gay abandon"! For example Mr H. who was suffering from gout, developed inflammation in one eye. He was seen by Mr George Norman and Dr Parry. "In the space of four days, twenty five ounces of blood were taken from the temporal artery of the same side, and seventy five ounces from the arm".[10]

Two groups of cases of blood diseases, Chlorosis and Purpura, were recognised clinically because of their obvious appearance, though their origin and nature was not understood. Both conditions could be diagnosed visually, and Parry recorded many cases of each. Chlorosis or Morbus Virgineus had been described as early as 1554 by Johann Lange. Parry's cases are described at the end of the second volume of "Collections". They were young women, some with amenorrhoea, and some with shortness of breath and palpitations on exertion. Various medicines were used, among them a mixture containing iron. Most recovered, but there is no suggestion that iron was considered an important or essential part of the treatment.

Parry also recorded many cases of Purpura. Two were described in a separate paper in 1809,[11] and the rest were included, by his son Charles, in the *Collections*. In 1809 a paper appeared in the Edinburgh Medical and Surgical Journal, on "Observations on the Utility of Venesection in Purpura. By C H Parry, Physician, Bath."

Ten or twelve years earlier, he had attended a lady about fifty years of age of "rather full habit" suffering from slight febrile symptoms. "Nothing else was worthy of attention but the state of her skin, which was thickly sprinkled with spots, small and of irregular forms, not raised above the surface, of a dark logwood colour, and in no degree evanescent on pressure." Mr Foster, an apothecary, who had called in Dr Parry for consultation, had bled the patient. Parry examined the blood, which had been standing some time, and noted that "the proportion of the whole crassamentum (clot) to that of the serum was uncommonly great". The patient had been much relieved by the venesection, which was repeated later. Soon after this he was called to see Colonel A. "in conjunction with Mr Atwood." The Colonel, "rather a free liver", was suffering from pyrexia due to severe epididymo-orchitis, which was not of venereal origin. Mr Atwood had been reluctant to bleed him because of "numerous logwood-coloured flat spots, which appeared on the skin, of different forms and sizes, some small, others as large as a silver penny . . . These spots as in the former case, were evidently ecchymoses, or extravasations of blood etc." Parry was satisfied from a comparison with the previous case "that no hazard would arise from blood lettings." The first venesection produced relief, and after a second one the spots disappeared. "The blood drawn had precisely the same appearance and tenacity as in the former instance."

Parry had no haematologists to help him. But it is suggested, that these two cases of purpura, relieved by repeated venesection, were cases of polycythaemia. That would appear to be the only description which would fit the relief of purpura by venesection with a blood specimen showing an excess of red cells ie. a larger proportion of the crassamentum to the remaining serum. It was only later, with all facilities, that Vaquez described the condition in 1892, followed by Osler in 1903. Parry calls attention, once more, to this early paper in his *Elements of Pathology and Therapeutics* (p. 126).

In the first volume of the posthumous *Collections* published by Charles Parry in 1825, there are records of several cases of purpura. The following patient is a textbook case.[12] On 21 January 1812 Parry saw Master W.T. aged nine years. The day before "about 3pm he complained of pain and soreness about the colon, and had frequent sickness and vomiting." On the day he was seen, "about 3 O'clock he had a motion with a little blood. . . . Today there have appeared on his legs many small flat spots, of a roundish form and various sizes. They are ecchymoses, and of a rather light red colour." Treatment was prescribed and the boy seen the next day. An enema of castor oil and egg yolk (!) "was soon followed by two motions with some fluid blood of a dark colour". He improved after some sleep, "his bowels being less sore, and in no degree tense or swelled . . . The spots on his legs and feet continue, and are of a somewhat darker colour than they were." He was bled, "the blood is of a dark colour and firm." By 23 January he had produced stools without blood but "the spots on his legs remain as before with regard to number, and are more brown than they were." He continued to improve, but some days later "he suffered a renewal of the petechial spots; but as he was about to return to London, I did not see him. There the disorder returned more than once preceded each time by some affection of the bowels, and was eventually cured, according to report (? postal follow-up), by spontaneous diarrhoea."

This was undoubtedly a case of Anaphylactoid purpura. Parry's description can hardly be mistaken for anything else. However, it is not the first description of what is commonly called Henoch Schonlein purpura. The first description was given by William Heberden[13] and appears in his *Commentaries* published in 1802. In Chapter 78 he described two boys with purpura of the lower limbs, the second of whom had "sometimes pains in his belly with vomiting, and at that time some streaks of blood were perceived in his stools, and the urine was tinged with blood. When the pain attacked his legs, he was unable to walk." Schonlein's paper on the association of purpura with articular disorders appeared in 1837[14] and in 1868, Henoch described the combination of purpura and abdominal pain.[15]

Tetanus and Rabies

Tetanus was recognised as a clinical entity as early as the Hippocratic collection in the fourth century B.C. The book of aphorisms contains the well known statement that a spasm supervening on a wound is usually fatal, and those attacked either die within four days, or if they survive this period they recover.[16] Rabies or hydrophobia was first described by Aetius of Amida in the sixth century A.D.[17] Rabies was the subject chosen by the young Parry in 1778 for his thesis for the Doctor of Medicine degree, and it was printed as a book in Edinburgh in 1778. It was dedicated to Lord Bathurst of Cirencester, the friend and patron of his father Joshua.

In 1814 Parry returned to the subject of rabies, and published his book *Cases of Tetanus and Rabies Contagiosa or Canine Hydrophobia etc*. It was dedicated to Edward Jenner, "my dear and oldest friend". His reason for writing the book was that "several cases of Canine hydrophobia having occurred in this city (Bath)" he was of the opinion that these two diseases, tetanus and rabies, had been confused in the literature, and he hoped to clarify the position.

The first section is devoted to tetanus. Parry had seen four patients. The first, a man of forty, had a leg amputated below the knee. On the fifth post-operative day he complained of pain in his head and throat and rigidity of his jaw. Parry found his head immoveably fixed, with rigidity of the muscles of the face and neck. He could neither open his mouth, nor swallow. Death followed despite treatment (bleeding and a glyster). Post mortem examination revealed a normal looking amputation stump. In the brain the vessels of the pia mater were distended with blood, but no other abnormality was discovered.

The second case, a boy aged five, had suffered a compound fracture

CASES

OF

TETANUS;

AND

RABIES CONTAGIOSA,

OR

CANINE HYDROPHOBIA;

WITH

REMARKS,

CHIEFLY INTENDED TO ASCERTAIN THE
CHARACTERISTIC SYMPTOMS OF THE LATTER DISEASE IN
MAN AND CERTAIN BRUTES,
AND TO POINT OUT THE MOST EFFECTUAL
MEANS OF PREVENTION.

BY

CALEB HILLIER PARRY, M.D. F.R.S.

Member of the College of Physicians of London; Fellow, and formerly President, of
the Royal Medical Society of Edinburgh; one of the Physicians of the
General Hospital at Bath; and Physician to the Casualty
Hospital and Puerperal Charity in that city.

PRINTED BY
RICHARD CRUTTWELL, ST. JAMES'S-STREET, BATH;
AND SOLD BY
UNDERWOOD, FLEET-STREET, LONDON.
1814.

Cases of Tetanus and Rabies Contagiosa

of the foot. On the eighth day he complained of difficulty opening his mouth. He was taken to the Casualty Hospital where he was seen by Mr George Norman, who put him on large doses of tincture of opium. However, he developed spasms and opisthotonos, and died later that day. A dissection was not permitted.

The third patient was a man aged thirty, who had a laceration of the left gastrocnemius sutured by Mr George Norman. This was followed two days later by gangrenous sloughing of the wound. The symptoms, stiffness in the back and jaw, developed twenty days later (an unusually long interval for true tetanus). He was given very large doses of tincture of opium for seven days, following which his spasms disappeared, and, although the wound was not completely healed, "he left the house at his own desire". It is unlikely that this was a case of tetanus, but it is interesting to note the use of heavy sedation in the treatment of the spasms.

A young woman, who had suffered severe frost bite leading to gangrene of several toes, was the fourth case. She was seen at the Casualty Hospital with stiffness of the jaw and her body bent rigidly forward. The disease took the usual relentless course. Post mortem examination by Mr George Norman revealed no gross lesion.

Parry puzzled about the origin and cause of the disease. He noted, from the literature, that the injury could be minimal, even the mere prick of a thorn. Within a short time, the patient was seized suddenly with muscular spasms and cramp like pain, especially in the muscles of the face, jaw and back. He had seen the same happen in lambs following branding of their ears – trismus, rigidity of the legs etc – and death usually followed within two to four days. He noted that cases without any injury had been recorded, where spasms occurred but full recovery was made. These patients did not have the rapid pulse, which was a feature of the fatal cases, and were probably not cases of tetanus. He also reported information received from Mr Sewell, "an ingenious veterinary surgeon", about the disease in four horses.

Another case of tetanus was seen by Parry in 1816, and is recorded in the first volume of the *Collections* of case notes published posthumously.[18] The patient was a man of fifty who had lacerated the back of his left leg. On the fifth day he developed difficulty opening his mouth, stiffness of the neck and back, and a cough. He died two days later. The post mortem findings include a description of pneumonia, probably lobar, supervening on the tetanus. There was "great congestion of blood in the lungs giving an appearance of solidity, like that of the liver . . . The lungs when cut into had scarcely any appearance of air."

The second and longer section of the book is devoted to Rabies Contagiosa, a name Caleb Parry preferred to Hydrophobia. The rarity of the disease is stressed – Edward Jenner, with access to the Berkeley kennels, had not seen a dog with rabies in forty years. Parry's experience consisted of three cases.

The first patient, a boy aged three, was bitten by a dog on 17 January 1807. There were no known mad dogs in Bath at that time, and as the dog ran off it could not be examined. The wound was sutured by Mr George Norman, and the child progressed satisfactorily for nearly two months. On 10 March he was unable to eat, and by the 12th he resisted any attempt to give him food or drink. His condition deteriorated rapidly and he died the next day. Permission was granted for a post mortem examination but no obvious lesion was found. The second patient, a man of thirty-five, was clinically similar, but there was no history of a dog bite. However, after his death, it was remembered that he had been bitten seven months earlier. Post mortem examination again showed no gross pathological findings. The third case, a five year old boy, was bitten on 22 May. His symptoms developed three weeks later, and lasted three days. Post mortem showed no gross lesion. This case shows a remarkable example of Parry's detailed notes. He visited the patient frequently, and his notes amount to sixteen pages. (This patient was also seen by Dr Crawford.)

The following is an example of the post mortem report on one of the patients, and it shows how astonishingly complete the examination was.

> Every part of the brain, medulla oblongata, larynx, trachea, lungs, heart, pericardium, pharynx, oesophagus, stomach, intestines, liver, gall bladder, pancreas, spleen, kidnies, and bladder, together with the meninges of the brain and the pleura and peritonaeum, was most carefully examined, both within and without, but in no part was there the least preternatural effusion, discoloration, or any deviation whatever from the healthy state.
>
> There having been no inflammation or pain in the wounded parts subsequently to the cicatrization, they were not opened.

Parry's fourth case was, he believed, not genuine but merely caused by terror of having rabies. Symptoms appeared two days after a dog bite and recovery occurred within a week.

As already noted, Parry stated in the Preface to his book that "much disagreement having taken place respecting the nature and symptoms", he thought it was time to review the cases reported in the literature, to show the characteristics of the true disease and to distinguish it from those that had been confused with it. He remarks "it was formerly doubted whether any such disease as Canine Hydrophobia existed".

The bulk of the book consists of a detailed review of previously published case reports. He distinguishes tetanus from rabies; the latter is always preceded by a bite from a dog, wolf or cat, it has a long incubation period, and lacks the widespread muscle spasms of tetanus, the symptoms of which, on the other hand, follow an open injury within a few days. He believed that the 'poison' which is the cause of rabies originated in the saliva of the dog. He also noted that in many cases of so-called rabies the symptoms developed a few days after a bite and the patient recovered. He rejects these as not being true examples of the disease. He also excluded other causes of difficulty with swallowing such as globus hystericus. No treatment appears to help, and the prognosis is gloomy. But he suggests that it may be worth trying early excision of the bite, and washing the wound with water "which should be long and assiduously employed". In all he lists thirty-eight cases which he considered to be genuine cases of rabies.

The only hope is prevention, and Parry ends the book with several pages of suggestions on the control of dogs. These include among others, a heavy tax on the owners of dogs, although in the case of stray dogs they can rarely be traced; the refusal of parish aid to any of the poor who own dogs; increased powers for magistrates to have dogs destroyed; and, if there is a mad dog in the area, to impose a period of three months' quarantine on all other dogs. He even drafted a model for a Bill to go before Parliament.

Elements of Pathology and Therapeutics

In 1815 Dr Parry published the first volume of his planned major work. In the Preface (July 1815) he regrets the delay in publication which "may have occasioned him some loss of credit". "The immediate exigencies of his profession have, however, so retarded the accomplishment of this design, that he every day sees announced as novelties, opinions, which for thirty years have formed the basis of his practice" Charles in the Preface to his *Introductory Essays* states "This abstract was prepared at the repeated solicitation of some of his

ELEMENTS

OF

PATHOLOGY AND THERAPEUTICS,

BEING THE

OUTLINES OF A WORK,

INTENDED TO ASCERTAIN THE

NATURE, CAUSES, AND MOST EFFICACIOUS MODES OF PREVENTION AND CURE, OF THE GREATER NUMBER OF THE DISEASES INCIDENTAL TO THE HUMAN FRAME;

ILLUSTRATED BY NUMEROUS CASES AND DISSECTIONS.

BY

CALEB HILLIER PARRY, M.D. F.R.S.

MEMBER OF THE COLLEGE OF PHYSICIANS OF LONDON;
MEMBER, AND FORMERLY PRESIDENT, OF THE ROYAL MEDICAL SOCIETY OF EDINBURGH;
ONE OF THE PHYSICIANS OF THE GENERAL HOSPITAL AT BATH, AND PHYSICIAN OF THE CASUALTY HOSPITAL, AND PUERPERAL CHARITY, IN THAT CITY.

VOL. I.

GENERAL PATHOLOGY.

SECOND EDITION.

PRINTED BY
RICHARD CRUTTWELL, ST. JAMES'S-STREET, BATH;
AND SOLD BY
UNDERWOOD, FLEET-STREET, LONDON.

1825.

Elements of Pathology and Therapeutics

friends. They were apprehensive, that, in delaying the publication of his opinions, under the hope of extending materials, which were already very considerable, and were daily accumulating in his hands, a final arrangement might either be entirely prevented, or, that the peculiarities, at least, which had been gradually adopted by many of those with whom the Author was in the habit of frequent intercourse and communication, might, at a subsequent period, cease to be redeemable as his own property." In the last chapter – "Recapitulation" – Caleb Parry says that he had "endeavoured to show that the far greater number of the diseases, incidental to the human frame, depends, . . . on excessive momentum of blood, whether local or general." He first put forward this theory in his paper in 1792 on carotid compression. Parry believed that most diseases, even many that had an obvious gross pathological basis, were due to "determination of the blood" i.e. the flow of blood to the diseased organ. Usually he was concerned with excessive determination, but he also recognised the opposite. He thought the theory was particularly important in diseases of the nervous system. He planned a work in two volumes, the first enunciating a collection of general principles and showing how his theory applied to the different systems of the body. The second volume, which he never wrote but had "long meditated" was to be "the very numerous cases and dissections, which are the proof of those principles . . ." "I have been able to record a considerable number of dissections, together with nearly seven hundred illustrative cases, which chiefly serve as the basis of my intended work." (Preface to Collections 1811.)

He was now very conscious of his deteriorating health, and in the preface to Elements of Pathology states that "If, however, it shall please Providence to frustrate that hope, the author has great satisfaction in leaving his materials in the hands of a person, (his son Charles), deservedly most dear to him, of whom it may be permitted him to assert, that his talents, as well as general and professional knowledge, render him fully competent to the execution of that task."

Of all Parry's works this is the most difficult to read and the least rewarding. It consists of over a thousand short paragraphs, pseudo-aphorisms or brief clinical observations, and some theoretical arguments. However a few of the comments are worth noting.

Perhaps the most noteworthy and original observation is paragraph LXIX. "It is one of the most important phaenomena of the animal frame, that after vessels have thus been more or less robbed of their blood, by the causes above specified, and many others, there often succeeds a contrary state, in which the vessels so robbed become unusually distended with blood, and the part, in consequence, preternaturally large, red, and hot, – a series of phaenomena very generally characterised by the term Reaction." Sir Thomas Lewis has pointed out that this is a clear description of reactive hyperaemia "It is indeed as he so stated and the term we use today is reactive hyperaemia, one of the most fundamental reactions of which the circulation is capable." So far as it has been possible to ascertain, this is probably the first description of this physiological reflex.

Other observations worth quoting are sometimes repetition of work already described, or they anticipate later publications. In discussing the motion of the blood Parry states in paragraph LVIII: "It is, indeed, sufficiently obvious that any alternate contractile power in the arterial system would just as much tend to impede the ingress of a new quantity of blood, as to promote the egress of that already existing in it; and, therefore, could in no degree assist the circulation." And later in paragraph XCV he says "The dissection of living animals shows, the ordinary tangible pulse being nothing more than the effort of a column of blood of a certain diameter to restore the area of a vessel artificially diminished by the pressure of the finger, or any other hard substance." These opinions were elaborated in the publication in 1816 of his book on the *Nature of the Arterial Pulse*. In paragraph CXX he repeats his earlier observations on the effect of carotid pressure in slowing the pulse. Paragraph CCCCLIII refers briefly to his observation on the association of enlargement of the thyroid gland with disease of the heart. The notes on the eight cases of hyperthyroidism he recorded did not appear in print until 1825. There may be many other notes of special interest or originality which have been overlooked.

The work was designed to support his theory, of the determination of the blood, the one serious error in his thinking. At the end of the book he sums up his belief. "This theory is of a very different character from those, which deduce the greater number of diseases from an assumed disorder of one particular viscus or local function. It is founded on an observation of certain like phaenomena, occurring in a system existing in every part of the body; and, therefore, constituting a law, under which are comprehended the affections, not of one part only, but of the whole frame." No reviews of this book have been traced, although some of the comments in Charles Parry's book of 1825 are replies to such criticisms, but it seems to have been sufficiently well received to justify a second edition three years after his death.

Arterial Pulse

In 1816 Parry published a book entitled *An Experimental Inquiry into the Nature, Cause, and Varieties of the Arterial Pulse . . . etc.* It was dedicated to Sir Joseph Banks, President of the Royal Society, whom Parry had come to know some years earlier, and with whom he had corresponded about his work on sheep breeding.

At the time Parry wrote this book, the nature of the pulse was still a matter of great controversy with several different explanations, and it remained so for many years. Twenty years later the situation was summed up by Palmer[19] in a footnote in the 1835 edition of John Hunter's *Treatise on the Blood*. Palmer writes that even at that date "physiologists are by no means perfectly agreed" on the matter. Palmer, clearly, placed most reliance on the reports of Haller, Majendie, Meckel etc who all claimed to have observed dilatation and contraction of the arteries, and this seems to have been the generally accepted explanation. However he does point out that "the diametrical enlargement of the artery was altogether denied by Parry, Laennec, and Bichat", but of those three Parry was the first to put forward the correct explanation. In 1811 when Caleb Parry and Mr George Norman were examining the vagus and sympathetic nerves in the necks of live animals, they "were astonished to observe, that, contrary to our preconceptions, the carotids, when exposed to view, were perfectly free from all dilatation during the systole of the left ventricle . . . except that they had a longitudinal locomotion backwards and forwards, exactly corresponding with the respiration . . ." The latter movement became more marked if the artery was freed from all the surrounding tissues. In all, fifty-five arteries were observed. Parry states in a footnote that this series is not included in his book.

In 1814 he started another series of experiments to see whether he could solve the problem of the nature of the pulse by direct observation of the arteries. He recorded a series of twenty-seven experiments on live animals, in whom, usually the carotid arteries, but also others eg. the femorals, were exposed and observed. Most of the dissections were done by his surgical colleague George Norman, whose name also appears frequently among Parry's case records when post mortem dissections were performed. There were always one or two independent witnesses present. The experiments were fitted in around his other work, sometimes in the early morning before the day's work had commenced, sometimes in the evening.

AN

EXPERIMENTAL INQUIRY

INTO THE

NATURE, CAUSE, AND VARIETIES

OF THE

ARTERIAL PULSE;

AND INTO

CERTAIN OTHER PROPERTIES

OF THE

LARGER ARTERIES,

IN ANIMALS WITH WARM BLOOD;

ILLUSTRATED BY ENGRAVINGS.

BY

CALEB HILLIER PARRY, M.D. F.R.S.

MEMBER OF THE COLLEGE OF PHYSICIANS OF LONDON;
MEMBER, AND FORMERLY A PRESIDENT, OF THE ROYAL MEDICAL SOCIETY OF EDINBURGH;
HONORARY MEMBER OF THE PHYSICAL SOCIETY OF GÖTTINGEN, AND OF THE GEOLOGICAL SOCIETY OF LONDON:
ONE OF THE PHYSICIANS TO THE BATH GENERAL HOSPITAL, AND PHYSICIAN TO THE CASUALTY HOSPITAL, AND PUERPERAL CHARITY, IN THAT CITY.

"TOTOS NOS IN CONTEMPLANDIS REBUS PERSPICIENDISQUE PONEMUS, PROPTEREA QUOD ET NATURA INEST MENTIBUS NOSTRIS INSATIABILIS QUÆDAM CUPIDITAS VERI VIDENDI."

CIC. TUSC. QUÆST. LIB. I.

PRINTED BY
RICHARD CRUTTWELL, ST. JAMES's-STREET, BATH;
AND SOLD BY
UNDERWOOD, FLEET-STREET, LONDON.
MDCCCXVI.

An Experimental Inquiry etc of the Arterial Pulse

The diameter of the artery was measured in 400ths of an inch using a fine compass, the arteries were then observed for movement under a powerful magnifying glass.

The experiments began on 22 September, 1814 at 8 a.m. when Mr George Norman exposed both carotid arteries in a ram in the presence of Dr Caleb Parry and Mr Coombs (see notes). The exposed carotids were examined carefully but no dilatation or contraction was observed. They were then ligated, and the ram walked off quite happily (?). Presumably, the vertebral arteries, though smaller in a sheep than the carotids, are still large enough to take over the intracranial blood supply.

Similar experiments followed, mostly using rams or ewes from Parry's own flock on Sion Hill, but occasionally using rabbits or dogs, or old horses which were due for slaughter. Parry's brother-in-law, Dr Edward Rigby of Norwich, was among a small group of onlookers at the fifth experiment on 8 June 1815. At the eighth experiment a visitor thought he could detect some expansion and contraction of the arteries, but no one else could agree. Charles is recorded as being present among the visitors at the fourteenth experiment on 4 September, 1815, at 3.30 p.m. He was also present at two later experiments.

Experiment 27 was started at 9.30 p.m. on 11 December, 1815. The dissection was done by Mr Coombs in the presence of Mr Chapman, Mr Wood and Dr Parry. An unsuccessful attempt was made to insert a goose quill into the left carotid artery. A crow quill was then introduced, but blood flowed out of the arterial wound around the quill. Parry writes "This experiment, however, is inconclusive". It must have been a very long day for Parry with the experiment starting at such a late hour, when it would have been done by candlelight or oil lamp, but his day did not end there. "Professional avocations prevented the further prosecution of the experiment at this time", in other words he was called out to see a case some time even later that evening. Clearly for a sixty year old man suffering from various diseases this was an extremely long and arduous day. The experiment was continued on 12 December, 1815, 9.30 a.m. The intact right carotid was exposed again and its circumference measured. "The ewe was then blooded from the left jugular vein, with the following effects on the circumference and other circumstances of the carotid artery, the action of the heart, and the respiration". The results were reported in tabular form.

With this long series of experiments completed, many observations noted and, in particular, with having satisfied himself and his visitors that no contraction or dilatation could be seen in the exposed arteries, Parry was in a position to make his contribution to the solution of the problems. He starts with a short chapter on the structure of the arteries. He recognised the usual three coats, but did not think that there was muscle in the middle coat. He took this view from the work of the chemist Berzelius, who believed that if muscle was present anywhere it could be recognised and confirmed chemically by the presence of fibrin. Berzelius was unable to demonstrate fibrin in arteries, but Parry recognised that arteries behaved as if muscular. This error probably contributed to some of the long and tortuous discussions in the next chapter on the Powers of Arteries.

There was general agreement that arteries possess the quality of elasticity "a merely mechanical power, in consequence of which, when forcibly distended, compressed or elongated, they spontaneously return to a mean state". There was, in addition, another "vital" factor of undetermined nature, that was that the wall behaved as though it was muscular. "The second is a vital faculty, presumed wholly to reside in the middle or fibrous coat; which has, therefore, been denominated muscular", but because Parry did not believe that it was muscular he called the contractile property "Tonicity".

The power of contraction was not difficult to observe. Hunter had already investigated the contractility of arteries. He isolated a segment of umbilical cord between two ligatures, ensuring that it was full of blood. When this segment was cut across, the blood flowed out and the empty vessels contracted immediately. He found that this property of contractility lasted quite a time, and was still present if the segment of cord was left as long as two days before cutting it open. He concluded that "the arteries, upon the whole, may be said to possess considerable living powers, and to retain them for a long time".[20] Parry was attached as Physician to the Puerperal Charity "of which the Messrs Norman are accouchers". With the help of Mr George Norman and Mr Coombs, he took advantage of the opportunities offered by this appointment to repeat Hunter's experiment. He agreed fully that when cut open at once the artery contracted after being emptied of blood, but he disagreed with Hunter about how long this power lasted. In his series Parry found that if the isolated segment was left for a day or more, the arterial opening remained patulous when emptied.

Parry investigated other aspects of the power of contraction in some of his experiments. He examined the effect of death on the behaviour of the arteries, by measuring the arteries before death, and then killing the animal by suffocation. Immediately after death the arteries were found to be reduced in diameter, but when re-examined twenty-one hours later there had been some dilatation, though not to the original size. Parry concluded that the immediate contraction was due to both powers of the arteries, ie. tonicity and elasticity. After death the vital power of tonicity disappears, and what remains is the effect of elasticity. Many measurements and calculations were made but the results were inconclusive, and at times contradictory.

The third set of circumstances investigated was the response of the arteries to reduction in the blood volume. In experiment twenty-seven, animals were bled and serial measurements made of the amount of blood removed and the size of the artery. Thus Parry demonstrated the fact that the arterial system contracted to compensate for the diminishing blood volume.

The most important chapter in the book is devoted to a discussion of the "Nature of the Pulse". As in all his books, Parry starts with an extensive review of the available literature. He considers the opinions of, and quotes extensively from, Haller, Bichat, and many more including Hales and Hunter, and shows that the opinion of the majority was that the pulse is due to successive dilatation and contraction of the arteries. He quotes from Rees's new *Cyclopaedia* ("a recent one, emanating from the metropolis . . ."), which states, under the article PULSE, "The pulse is well-known to consist of the successive dilatations and contractions of the arteries, in consequence of the successive impulses given to the blood through them by the repeated contractions of the heart, and by their own muscular and elastic powers". This view, as already noted, was still held by Palmer twenty years later.

However, Bichat and Hunter, had recognised, as Parry and George Norman had, that when an artery was exposed and denuded, no contraction or dilatation could be discerned. They too had observed that the whole artery, when freed, showed a thrusting movement. Two movements were described, a large displacement coinciding with respiration, and a smaller movement coinciding with systole of the ventricles. They each proposed different explanations for the palpable pulse. Bichat's was the simplest. He believed that there was "change of place in the whole artery: in consequence of which, it springs against the finger during the systole, and returns during diastole". John Hunter's explanation was surprising[21] and full of contradictions. Having observed that the exposed artery mainly showed movement of elongation and retraction with cardiac systole he states "It is, however, the increased diameter that becomes sensible to the touch". But he goes on to note that in laying an artery bare "its motion is hardly to be either felt or seen. The more an artery is covered, especially with solid bodies, the more is the pulsation to be felt or seen". Thus although he could not observe contraction and dilatation in the exposed artery, Hunter, most unusually, produced an illogical explanation for the palpable pulse. As Parry comments ". . . no one ever felt a pulse in a living body at all better, because a thick garment, or a steel gauntlet, intervened between the artery and the scrutinising finger. On the contrary, the pulse of an artery . . . is better felt . . . when it is superficial, than when it is deep". And he illustrates this by noting the ease of palpation in the radial compared with carotid, or popliteal or femoral arteries.

Parry then set out to explain his view of what made the pulse palpable and what it was that was being felt. He had shown repeatedly in his experiments that the pulse could not be felt unless the exposed artery was compressed between the fingers or against a firm structure, thus reducing its cross-sectional area. He believed that "when, by the contraction of the left ventricle the blood included in it is forcibly expelled into the aorta, all these columns (ie the arteries) receive the shock of propulsion at the same instant". "Hence, it appears, that the pulse is the effect, not of an extension of an artery beyond its usual diameter, but of a stronger effort . . . to restore the usual diameter of the artery, which had been diminished by compression". He also pointed out that arterial contraction "would just as much tend to impede the ingress of a new quantity of blood, as to promote the egress of that already existing in it; and, therefore, could in no degree assist the circulation".[22]

In his book[23] Charles Parry published a copy of a letter of his father's "which has not been seen by many of his friends". The letter is a defence by Caleb Parry of his views which had received wide criticism. In it he provides a clear analogy to explain what he believes causes the pulse. "I consider the blood globules . . . incompressible; and, in this view, they are like a series of billiard-balls in close contact with each other; so that if an impulse is made from behind, immediately the foremost ball, however distant is moved". Sir Thomas Lewis[24] writes "We express very similar ideas today in speaking of the arterial pulse as a pressure wave as opposed to a wave of volume", and he credits Parry with the first accurate explanation of the mechanism of the pulse.

The last part of the book discusses the growth of anatomoses around the ligated carotid in the ram. Some animals were re-examined a year or so later and then slaughtered. The carotids were injected and carefully dissected by Mr Coombs which revealed the presence of arterial channels joining the two ends. The dissections were drawn by Charles Parry who, in his younger days, had won prizes for his artistic skill. Caleb believed that these were new formations, not dilatation of existing channels, because at the original operation the carotids had been stripped bare and were free of any branches. But he admitted that further work would have to be done on a larger number of animals before a firm decision could be made.

Parry's book on the nature of the pulse was his last major work to be published during his life time. A few months later in the same year he was immobilised by a stroke. In 1819 his son Charles published a book in which he defended his father's opinions and recorded some of the experiments that had not been completed at the time of publication of Caleb's book.[25]

Note

Mr Coombs appears to have been a pupil or trainee of Dr Parry. Bath Reference Library possesses a letter of recommendation written by Parry for Mr William Coombs, presumably the same man who assisted and later performed some of the experiments.

> Understanding that it is the intention of Mr William Coombs of this City to offer himself as a candidate for a responsible situation in the Infirmary of Manchester, I think it an act of justice to the character of that excellent young man to relate of him that which I personally know, and have every where heard of him from persons of credit, with whom he is most intimately connected.
>
> He is of morals which cannot be impeached, modest and unassuming, sedulous and punctual in business, and indefatigable in the cultivation of professional knowledge, his opportunities of attaining which have been unusually extensive, and of which he has fully availed himself.
>
> I have, therefore, no hesitation in affirming that he is fully competent to the situation which he solicits, and in expressing my belief that he will fill it to his own credit, and to the advantage of the charity.
>
> On these subjects I speak with the greatest confidence from having well known him during his attendance at the Casualty Hospital in the City, of which I am Physician.
>
> (Signed) C H Parry, M.D.
>
> Bath, July 26th, 1814.

CHAPTER 9

Posthumous Publications

In 1825 Charles Parry published a second edition of the *Elements* because, he says, of the interest in and recognition of the merits of his father's "chief work". The new edition contained the few pages that were the beginning of the planned second volume. The book was accompanied by a volume of *Introductory Essays* by Charles Parry.[1] In this prolix book Charles attempted to explain and justify his father's theory of determination of the blood. He wrote "it has never been denied that this doctrine received a very full elucidation from the industry and original researches of Dr Parry." He considered this book to be his father's most important contribution to medicine – his chief work. Reviews of the two books have been found, and generally the theory of determination of the blood was no better received than when it was first propounded.

In May 1825 the *Lancet* quoted large sections of the *Elements of Pathology* but the reviewer was not happy with Caleb Parry's explanations for many conditions. However, he described it as the more valuable because "it is the production of a cultivated mind in the plenitude of experience and maturity of years".[2] Anderson's *Quarterly Journal* in July 1825[3] described the *Elements of Pathology* as "this celebrated work . . . well known to our readers." In October 1825[4] another review appeared in the same journal dealing with the accompanying *Introductory Essays* by Charles Parry. The reviewer wondered whether a whole book was necessary, and suggested that Charles Parry's defence of his father's views might have been better contracted into a preface to the work "now in the course of publication". Of one section the reviewer commented ". . . the author has made the following remarks which have the merit of being intelligible". The *London Medical Repository*[5] considered Charles Parry's *Introductory Essays* as "altogether controversial", and they looked forward to "the prospect of having collections from the unpublished writings of the late Dr Parry placed before them."

Collections from the Unpublished Medical Writings of the Late Caleb Hillier Parry M.D. F.R.S. London 1825

Caleb Parry had planned his last major work five years before his stroke in 1816, and during that period he had collected and selected from his notes the material that he intended to use. The long preface to this work was written as early as October 1811, four years before he published *Elements of Pathology and Therapeutics*, which was the first volume of the planned work and which had its own short preface dated 1815. As early as 1811 his health was causing sufficient anxiety for him to express doubts as to whether he had "any reasonable chance of reaching the end of my proposed journey". Charles was not surprised that the work had not been completed by his father before his stroke. He writes of his father "in his most vigorous health he had never possessed those facilities, which, to most writers, have appeared necessary for the proper arrangement of the materials which may have been collected in the hurry of the world's affairs. He was totally unacquainted with leisure and seclusion."[6]

The preface to *Collections* is a statement of Caleb Parry's scientific and medical philosophy. The most dangerous state incidental to the human mind is, he says, "a calm acquiescence in the accuracy and extent of its own attainments." The preface discusses the importance of basic knowledge, not only of anatomy, physiology, pathology and therapeutics, but also of more general subjects such as numbers, mechanics, botany and chemistry, Latin and other European languages. Parry stressed the importance of logic and the dangers of false reasoning leading to wrong conclusions. He considered that the low status of doctors was due to the neglect of these principles. "It is a painful duty for me to remark, that there is no subject in life, in which more of false reasoning is admitted than in the practice of Medicine."

Dr Parry had selected about 700 case reports and many post mortem reports to form the basis of the second part of the work, and Charles was left with the task of turning these papers, and some general essays into a book. In 1824 Charles Parry noted that he had approached the task of completing his father's work with apprehension, because the notes, as they had been left, were not in a fit state for publication.[7] However he succeeded in arranging and grouping them, and late in 1825 he published a two-volume work containing a collection of his father's meticulous detailed case notes. The resulting publication contained in its 1,100 pages much of interest

UNPUBLISHED

MEDICAL WRITINGS

OF THE LATE

CALEB HILLIER PARRY,

M. D. F. R. S. &c. &c. &c.

VOL I.

LONDON:

UNDERWOODS, FLEET-STREET,

1825.

Collections from the unpublished Medical Writings etc 1825

and importance, which was not realised by Charles Parry. Charles believed that the *Elements of Pathology and Therapeutics*, which he had republished earlier that year, was his father's greatest work, otherwise "little would have remained to do justice to his memory".[8] This seems to have been the general opinion. Mainwaring[9] writes "The greatest and most characteristic work of this eminent philosopher and physician was his *Elements of Pathology*, published in 1816, which is professionally considered as an almost unparalleled example of great originality and capacity, combined with profound research and observation."

During the time that Parry practised medicine there were no ancillary aids to examination and diagnosis. There were no stethoscopes, there was as yet no understanding of bacteriology or cellular pathology, and X-rays were unrecognised. The doctor had to make his diagnosis from what the patient told him and from what his eyes and hands discovered. There was one possible objective aid. John Hunter had sent Jenner a thermometer to help with his experiments on the hibernation of hedgehogs, and Parry probably knew about it. It is almost certain that he, too, possessed a thermometer. It is remarkable that neither Jenner nor Parry thought of using the thermometer to record their patients' temperatures. In 1612 Sanctorius had described a thermometer and had suggested its use in the study of human patients. George Martine of Scotland in *Essays and Observations* (1710) wrote the first work on clinical thermometry, and it is surprising that this does not appear to have been known to Parry. The classic work on temperature in disease was by C.R.A. Wunderlich in 1868. Garrison writes "he found fever a disease and left it a symptom". Parry did not, so far as is known, use the thermometer to measure his patients' temperatures, but reference to it does appear in the case notes e.g. "I wish a tepid bath at 92° to be used twice a week."

The book cannot be described as a textbook. Even though it was meant to illustrate the theory of determination of the blood, that theme is not stressed nor mentioned in most of the case records. One chapter is devoted to the theory, but Parry was aware of the criticism of his earlier advocacy of determination as an explanation of nervous diseases. Later in the book he writes "My medical creed on the subject of nervous complaints, is thought in the highest degree heterodox, and subjects me to the pains and penalties . . . made and provided by my medical brethren."[10]

The book is essentially a collection of the case notes of hundreds of interesting patients selected from the records kept by a busy physician over a period of thirty-seven years. It gives a wonderful, and presumably representative, picture of the medical practice of a popular physician during those years. The lucid case notes vary from the very brief to the very detailed and lengthy. Many of the reports include progress notes of the illness, and a few contain copies of letters sent to the patient's doctor, or to the patient, giving detailed instructions for treatment.

The number and scope of the post mortem dissections, usually carried out by a surgical colleague, but attended and described by Caleb Parry, is most impressive. An example of the scope of a full post mortem examination has been given in an earlier section. Only the naked eye appearances were noted, unsupported by microscopical examination, which had not yet been introduced. Refrigeration was not available, and some of the appearances seen and described were probably due to normal post mortem changes. It is, of course, impossible to be sure how much of the text was as Caleb Parry left it and how much, if at all, the case notes were rewritten or edited by Charles.

The question of priority seems to have plagued medical authors as much two hundred years ago as it does today. Caleb Parry himself had been worried about the priority of his views, but he was concerned more with general theories and methods of practice, which he claimed were being adopted and described by other people years after he had used them. The *Collections* although originally intended to confirm his theory of determination of the blood, is now recognised for the fact that it contains the first known descriptions of several diseases and symptoms. The problem is that the records were not published until 1825, three years after Parry's death. The present author is in no position to express an opinion on claims for priority for the recognition and description of a disease, and he has been guided by the standard authorities.

Can priority be claimed for such delayed records? The outstanding example is Parry's classic description of his first case of thyrotoxicosis seen in 1786. Sir William Osler recognised this as the earliest description of the disease and suggested that the condition should be called Parry's disease. Flajani described the condition in 1802, but Osler considered the date of Parry's account sufficient reason to credit him with the earliest description in spite of the late date of publication, and this is accepted now. The eponym most commonly used is "Graves' Disease". Graves described three cases in 1835.

A selection of case notes follow, for some of which priority is claimed, some which may be the earliest or very early record, and some have been included simply to illustrate the clarity of Parry's notes and excellence of his recording.

Thyrotoxicosis

In 1786 Parry recorded his first case of "Enlargement of the Thyroid Gland in connection with Enlargement or Palpitation of the Heart."[11] "There is one malady which I have in five cases seen coincident with what appeared to be enlargement of the heart, and which, so far as I know, has not been noticed, in that connection, by medical writers. The malady to which I allude is enlargement of the Thyroid gland". Three more cases were added when the book was published. The function of the thyroid gland was not understood at that time. In *Elements of Pathology* Parry noted that the thyroid gland had no known excretory duct, and its use was "hitherto undiscovered".

In 1786 he saw Grace B, a woman of thirty-seven. Six years earlier she developed a lump in her neck which had enlarged. This was followed by increasing palpitations of the heart. When seen, her heart beat "was so vehement that each systole shook the whole thorax". Her pulse was 156 and irregular. She had oedematous swelling of her legs and thighs, and scanty urine. "The part swelled was the thyroid gland . . . the eyes protruded from their sockets." He saw her several times and ends his notes thus: "From this time no farther application was made to me respecting this patient, who, probably, soon paid her debt to nature."

As noted earlier Sir Sydney Parry recorded in his family notes receiving a visit in 1907 from Sir William Osler, who was the first to recognise Parry's claim for priority for the recognition of exophthalmic goitre. Osler called it Parry's disease, and some later authors have used the same title for their papers. Fifty years ago the name was used regularly by the senior surgeon in Bath.

Singular and Fatal Accumulation of Faeces

Doctor C was seen by Dr Parry only a few days before his death.[12] Some six months earlier he had developed colic, nausea, and loose stools, which he attributed to indurated faeces. The condition progressed. In spite of "recourse to powerful purgatives, constipation ensued, and continued with severe pain, sickness, and vomiting."

Later "faecal vomiting seems, by the patient's own account, to have taken place." When seen by Dr Parry he had a swollen abdomen. "The faeculent eructations and vomiting continued to the end of life." Post mortem was done by Mr Norman senior. The colon was dilated and almost black. "The dilatation of the colon extended to about the beginning of the sigmoid flexure, where it resumed nearly its natural size". This is the first description of what is now called Idiopathic Dilatation of the Colon. It was described by Hirschsprung in 1887 and is commonly referred to by his name, but it is now accepted generally that it was first described by Parry.

Facial Hemiatrophy

This is a rare condition and most doctors will go through their clinical lives without ever seeing a sufferer. Parry has given the earliest description of this condition.[13] The patient, Miss F., aged twenty-eight, had an attack thirteen or fourteen years before seeing Dr Parry, the nature of which "it is now impossible to ascertain". Starting in childhood the left side of her face grew less than the right and appeared smaller. The hair on the left side became white while it remained brown on the right side. This condition was described later (1846) by Romberg in Berlin, and is called the Parry-Romberg disease by some authors.

Mitral Stenosis with Aneurysmal Dilatation of the Auricle

Two patients were seen by Dr Parry, in 1798 and in 1813.[14] Both died with symptoms of heart failure, and in both cases permission for post mortem examination was obtained.

Mr T.B. ("always very temperate with regard to wine, and extremely attentive to a very profitable business") is classified as "Enlarged Heart from Ossification of the Mitral Valves, and Annulus Venosus." At post mortem the thorax "contained a heart of a most stupendous size," mostly due to the enlarged auricles, the right containing nine ounces and the left thirteen ounces of "coagulum". Both auricles were "preternaturally" thin, "the left almost like a membrane." "One of the mitral valves was completely ossified . . . the whole opening between the auricle and ventricle was so contracted as scarcely to admit the point of the little finger."

Mr J.T. ("a man of excellent moral and religious principles") seen in 1813 had an "Enlarged Heart, with incompetent function in the

Tricuspid (?and) Mitral Valves." Parry saw him during the last ten days of his illness. At post mortem "his thorax was opened by Mr White, in my presence, *at ten o'clock at night*. The auricles were thin and very large." The tricuspid and mitral valves were extremely rigid, almost cartilaginous at their bases. "On the whole, it was evident that both the tricuspid and mitral valves were in such a state as to be incapable of preventing the regurgitation of part of the blood into the auricles during the contraction of the ventricles at each systole of the heart." Sir Thomas Lewis considered that these were cases of aneurysmal dilatation of the auricles, and said he knew of no earlier account.[15]

Hay Fever

The first modern description of hay fever is generally attributed to John Bostock in 1819. Parry recorded a patient in 1809 with symptoms which he called asthma but some of which were surely due to hay fever.[16] His patient, an opulent gardener aged about thirty, was generally well, but in the middle of May felt "a tightness and fullness in his nose, which is stuffed so that he can scarcely breathe through it . . . The complaint then leaves the nose, and his eyes become red sore and watery." "Mr P not only always found his asthmatic paroxysm aggravated in the summer, by standing in a hay field merely looking at the haymakers making the hay-rick, but has often found difficulty of breathing produced in the winter when he has stood near old hay putting into a hay-loft from off a cart."

Some interesting case reports

Non-obstructive jaundice

No note has been found, in the historical bibliographies consulted, of when the distinction was made between obstructive and non-obstructive or haemolytic jaundice. Nor has reference been found to the development of jaundice in malaria. In 1796 Parry noted that "the jaundice in the cold fit of an ague depends on the blood accumulated in the liver, producing more secretion than can be carried off. The urine is dark coloured, though the stools are dark also. There is therefore no obstruction."

Wrist drop from lead poisoning

Paralysis of the hands arising from lead poisoning was well known before Parry's time, and is seen in the portrait, by William Hoare, showing Mr Jerry Pierce and Dr William Oliver examining a sufferer. However, it is interesting to note its frequency. Parry writes "for many years past I have rarely been without from six to twelve patients labouring under this disease."

There are many more excellent and interesting case reports, including the treatment of oedema with digitalis, heart block, several more cases of angina seen after the publication of his book, a blue baby, aortic stenosis, epididymo-orchitis following mumps, a series of cases of chlorosis, and many more. There is a long and detailed section on renal calculus based on his own experience.

Parry's writings contain few light-hearted or amusing remarks. However two of his cases are worth noting, uncertain though it is whether they were included seriously, or with tongue in cheek.

Miss T, aged 14, who had a vast catalogue of symptoms, also "had a slight attack of the usual song". She "lay on her back . . . threw out her left arm . . . exactly keeping time with the following notes, which she sang out with a strong clear voice." Dr Parry recorded the tune in musical notation and his son has included it in the book.[17]

Mr A, "a great dram drinker", gave a curious reason for his dropsy when Parry saw him "labouring under ascites, anasarca, and jaundice". He said "I had been with a friend with whom I dined, and drank a cheerful glass, but according to my custom very temperately. I was always used to keep a bottle of gin by my bedside, of which I sometimes drank a teaspoonful or two during the night. On this unfortunate night, feeling my stomach not well, I put out my hand and reached the bottle, of which I drank, but did not discover that by mistake I had taken water, till I had drank nearly half a pint. I felt it very cold in my stomach, and immediately endeavoured as well as I could to counteract the injury by the gin, of which I drank about two glasses. It proved however, that the quantity which I drank was not sufficient, and in consequence of this inexcusable negligence, I was taken with my dropsy on the Tuesday following".[18]

CHAPTER 10

The Parry Library

The Hospital Library and Parry Collection

A notable feature of all Caleb Parry's works, whether medical or agricultural, is the extensive references he makes to books by other writers, ancient and contemporary, and also to articles in scientific and medical publications. Inevitably one must wonder where or how all this material was available to him. As a student in Edinburgh, when he wrote his graduation thesis on Rabies, he would have had the use of the large and growing library of the students' Royal Medical Society, as well as the University Library. But what libraries were there in Bath when he settled there in 1779? His own library could only have been built up gradually over the years.

The library of Bath Abbey is said to have contained collections of books presented to it, over a long period by doctors.[1] Kite[2] says that this library was poorly funded and neglected from the start. It was forgotten for years until 1866 when it was discovered, and thirty years later it was presented to the City. This library could not have been a source of information for Parry.

The medical institutions, when Parry settled in Bath, were the General Hospital and the Pauper Charity. Rolls[3] states that he has not found any record of a library at the General Hospital until 1910, when Sir William Osler donated a gift of £10 to the hospital to help start one. The Pauper Charity, which was mainly a domiciliary service, was unlikely to have had a library, and the two later foundations which Parry served, the Casualty Hospital and the Puerperal Charity were also unlikely to have had a collection of books. Kite does not record any specialist medical libraries in Bath at this time.[4] To cater for its large visiting population, eighteenth century Bath had many bookshops and lending libraries. In his historical review of Bath libraries, Kite records the association of these libraries with doctors or medical books.

The first important Bath bookseller and publisher of a medical book was James Leake (b. 1686) who published Dr George Cheyne's *Essay of Health and Long Life* in 1724. Leake was a well respected member of the community, and served on the committee of the General Hospital. His library was frequented by and became a meeting place for the local notables. In 1770 it changed its name to Bull's Circulating Library but continued to be a central meeting place. In his later years Dr Henry Harington was to be found sitting at Bull's library in his full bottomed wig, with his three cornered hat, completely blind, chatting sociably and full of animation.[5] Whether Bull's library contained a medical or scientific section at that time is unclear, but the 1796 catalogue of Hazard's in Cheap Street shows that it catered for professional men. The index lists subjects which include Physic and Surgery, Sciences, Natural History, Agriculture, Botany etc. Parry's active medical life ceased in 1816 but it is of interest to note some of the developments over the next few years. Libraries devoted to one subject were rarely found, but in 1819 Bull's successor, John Upham, advertised that for a separate subscription "he has annexed to his library a department . . . appropriated to medicine, natural history and the several branches of natural philosophy." Several years later (1858) Hayward and Davies opened "a circulating medical library, in connection with a celebrated London library, comprising a choice of several thousand volumes in medicine, surgery, and the collateral sciences."[6]

In the Preface to his second book on sheep and wool,[7] after listing his main source material Parry writes "It is on occasions like these that I regret my distance from a University or the Capital; but I have the greatest pleasure in publicly expressing how much that want has been lessened by the free use of the valuable library of my excellent and learned friend Dr Falconer."

There must have been other doctors in Bath besides Dr Falconer who had collected their own libraries; and, presumably, these collections usually passed from one generation to the next, but some were probably sold at sales or in second hand bookshops. Journals and magazines must have been obtained by personal subscription, or possibly by some sharing arrangement. No evidence for sharing has been found during Caleb Parry's lifetime but in 1839 fifteen doctors formed the Bath Medical Book Society. The plan was to buy books by using the subscriptions from the members. After a time the books were put up for sale by auction among the members. This society thrived and grew for quite a time. In 1845 there were twenty members, and in 1860 there were forty-five.[8]

In his writings Parry not only refers to many books, but also to many periodical publications. No attempt has been made to list all the journals he refers to in his many works, but some idea can be obtained from a partial analysis. In the last part of his book on Tetanus and Rabies Contagiosa,[9] he has listed thirty-eight cases of the latter disease reported in England, which he considers to have been true accounts of rabies, and he has given the sources of the reports. This list provides an interesting picture of some of the books and journals he had consulted. Most of the cases were reported in books but fourteen were reported in journals. These were checked by consulting the list of the English medical journals made by LeFanu which includes the dates of publications.[10] Some of the journals had already ceased publication by the time Parry wrote his book, and may have been seen by him in Edinburgh when he wrote his M.D. thesis. Whether Parry subscribed to all the rest or they were available among his colleagues is unclear. One way or other, by the purchase of new and second-hand books, and possibly even whole collections, (cf Geology) he built up a large library which was housed at Summerhill.

Charles continued to add to the library after his father's death. In 1845 he decided to leave Summerhill, and he sold the contents, and offered the library to the United Hospital.[11] It is not clear why Charles chose the United Hospital and not the General Hospital for his gift. He had been on the staff of the General Hospital for four years, whereas he does not appear to have served on the staff of the new United Hospital. He writes[12] "I was chosen Senior Physician, but, on a large view of the case, a consideration of its unprofitableness, and the great devotion of time which it required, declined the offer."

His letter lays down some conditions which appear to imply that there was no pre-existing library at the United Hospital, and no other evidence for a library has been found. The minutes of a meeting on Monday 29 September, 1845 record:

6. The following letter from Dr Parry was read.

Copy.
My dear Norman,

I submit the following proposition to the members of the United Hospital as time presses much, hope to receive an answer in 2 or 3 days. The books must otherwise be sold to make room for Painters and other workmen.

I propose to give to the Governors and Trustees of the Hospital for the time being for the use of the Medical Establishment these all my Father's and my own medical library on the following conditions.

1st That these Volumes *shall never be sold* or if such a necessity should . . . arise, that the property in them shall revert to myself or Heirs.

2nd That considering the value of such a collection proper shelves shall be put up in a suitable place for its reception.
3rd That due care shall be taken of the Books and such restriction placed upon their use, and shall secure them from loss, or material injury.
4 That myself on . . . shall at all times be allowed the free use of them when required.
5 That should there be no immediate accommodation for them, they be deposited for the present in some secure and vacant room engaging myself when shelves are prepared to . . . their arrangement and to supply a Catalogue.
These conditions seem to be equitable for all parties.

Yours etc.
Charles H Parry
September 27, 1845

6 Resolved that the best thanks of the Trustees and Committee be tendered to Dr Parry for his valuable donation of medical books and that this same be accepted on the conditions proposed.

A sub-committee was formed "to communicate with Dr Parry and carry this resolution into effect," it resolved further that this donation be specially mentioned in the next report.

In April 1846 there is a minute stating that an inscription was to be "put over the Bookcase containing the Books presented to the Hospital by Dr Parry recording his munificent gift."

In a book published in 1854, Monkland[13] refers to Dr Charles Parry, with whom he was at school, and notes that "He has munificently presented to the United Hospital his father's valuable medical library." A neighbour,[14] who owns a copy of Monkland's book, which belonged originally to Dr R. Wilbraham Falconer, reports that Dr Falconer has underlined the words "valuable medical" and noted against it "The whole?". Did Charles sell part of the library with the sale of the rest of the contents of Summerhill? Brian Jones[15] notes "I recently received a letter from someone who had bought two books bearing Parry's bookplate which do not appear to have been in the collection even when Bath Reference Library catalogued it in the 1930's . . ." In 1876 the Minutes of the Royal United Hospital contain the following entry. "The Chaplain requested permission for a scroll over the Communion Table in the Chapel, the expense to be defrayed by the sale of superfluous Library Books." In 1876 the library probably consisted only of the Parry and Soden collections.[16] No record of a sale has been found.

The library remained in the Royal United Hospital in the old building in Beau Street (now part of the Technical College). It received various additions, notably Dr Soden's library in 1863.[17]

In 1925 the British Medical Association held its annual conference in Bath. There was considerable interest in Caleb Parry, and a plaque was placed at 27 Circus. Mr John Hatton, Director of the Spa, in a paper in the *B.M.J.*[18] records that "he (Parry) has left in his published writings and *in the notebooks which are carefully preserved in the library of this hospital* (Royal United), the record of a scientific mind . . ." No trace of, nor other reference to, these notebooks has been found. Sir Sydney Parry,[19] writing about the same time, says that Sir William Osler was responsible for arranging and making a catalogue of the library, but no confirmatory evidence has been found.

Problems for the library arose when it was decided to move the hospital from its old inadequate building in the centre of the town to a spacious site on the periphery at Combe Park. The new building would be close to the Bath and Wessex Children's Orthopaedic Hospital and the Forbes Fraser private hospital. No provision was made for the library. There followed a period of committees and suggestions. First it was proposed to offer the collection to the Royal College of Physicians or the Royal College of Surgeons, but Mr Leonard Fuller pointed out that this would contravene the original conditions of the gift.[20] At the request of the Managing Board the Medical Board set up a sub-committee to decide for how many volumes it would be necessary to provide accommodation *"after those of no interest had been destroyed"*.[21, 22] Later the library was offered to the City on permanent loan, an offer which the Council accepted.[23] The minute recommended that:

> arrangements be made for the library, which comprises the world famous libraries of Dr Caleb Hillier Parry and his son Dr Charles H Parry, Dr Hunter's collection of medical treatises and tracts and other collections of books of medical and bibliographical interest (*the whole library consisting of upwards of 4000 volumes*), as set forth in part and in detail in the MS Catalogue of the Library, Bath United Hospital, to remain at the Hospital until such time as suitable accommodation can be obtained for the conservation of this medical library under the care of the Corporation.

This was reported back to the hospital.[24] The reply to an enquiry by the Hospital Secretary confirmed that the Council had no accommodation for the library, which was therefore left in the old building.[25] During the War (1939–45) precautions were taken to provide safe storage of Library Treasures, but this probably did not include the hospital library, which appears to have remained at the old hospital.[26]

In 1948 Reginald W.M. Wright, published an article on the Bath Hospital Medical Library, which was still in the care of the City.[27] The last paragraph is interesting:

> The Parry library is indeed unique and it is natural that in this collection the works and *pamphlets* by Caleb Hiller Parry are fully represented. The hospital library *as a whole* has been in the possession of the Bath Library Authority as a permanent loan for some fifteen years. It was handed over to the library committee when the hospital was removed to Combe Park. During this period of loan the library was accessed, catalogued and classified by Mr Arthur Mellor who was then on the staff of the Reference Library.

The article also gives a short review of medical libraries in Bath and describes some of the more noteworthy books in the hospital collection.

In the same year the Medical Board of the R.U.H.[28] was discussing the possibility of its transfer "to the Historical Section of the B.M.A. Library – so that it can be made more available to the profession as a whole". Mr Reginald Wright was invited to a meeting of the medical staff in May 1948, and explained that copies of all Parry's books were already available in the London libraries.[29] It was therefore recommended that the Parry Library, now on loan to the City Library "be made a free gift to the City Council", but in July 1948 the Council declined the offer "of the Parry and Soden Medical Library". They suggested that the library be offered to the City of Bristol.[30]

On 28 July, 1948 under the heading "Doctors' Library Gift to City: Space Problem" the local newspaper reported the efforts of councillor C.E. Kindersley, Senior Surgeon at the Royal United Hospital, to keep the library in Bath. He forecast that "Bath was going to be a considerable medical centre".[31] However, in March 1949 the Town Clerk reported that after negotiations between the Charity Commissioners and the Ministry of Health it was agreed that the library was "transferable to the Minister",[32] and on 7 February 1950 he "reported that the whole of the Parry Medical Library had now been transferred to the University of Bristol".[33]

The Medical Staff at the Royal United Hospital were sorry to lose the library but were glad that it was remaining in the area. There was no place in the hospital or elsewhere on the Combe Park site for such a valuable collection to be housed securely and safely.

In a recent lecture Brian Jones has given a summary of the history of the library since its transfer to Bristol.[34] By the time of transfer many of the books were in a poor condition but, with the help of grants from the Wellcome Trust and University funds, repairs were carried out. Some of the books have been absorbed into the general arrangement of the Bristol University Medical Library, but the bulk of the "Parry Collection" is housed in the locked Medical History Room. Some of the books have Caleb Parry's bookplate and some have Charles's. But the ownership of a large number cannot be proved, and some were probably those donated by Dr John Soden.

It is not certain that all the books are in Bristol. Mr Roberts, Librarian at the time of the transfer, has noted that the books had remained neglected for so many years that anything could have happened to them. It is impossible to guess what happened to the bulk of the 4000 volumes, but about 900 are now safely housed.

A large amount of the material relating to the Parry library has been provided by Mrs Kate Clarke to whom I am indebted. Mrs Clarke recently retired from the post of Senior Area Librarian at the Royal United Hospital, Bath. Shortly before she retired she noticed a skip full of books in a room in the hospital. On investigation she found the books to be the old minute books of the hospital up to its incorporation into the NHS – in other words the rubbish skip contained the only written records of the hospital's history. The recently appointed hospital manager had come directly from industry, with no medical background and no interest in the history of the institution he was managing. Mrs Clarke salvaged the books, and found a home for them in the City Archives, where she is painstakingly sorting out the most important historical records. I am also grateful to Mr Jones, retired librarian Bristol Medical Library, for permission to quote from his MSS notes of a talk on Parry.

Appendices

Premiums given to Dr Caleb Parry or to clothiers using his wool by the Bath and West Society.

1796	To Dr Parry of Bath for the second best (fleece) Plate	3-3-0
1798	To Dr Parry, in consideration of his great care and attention to the improving the quality and value of a Fleece of Wool, without increasing the weight of the animal, etc etc.	3-0-0
1799	To Dr Parry, for the most valuable crop of Cabbages for cattle.	5-5-0
1800	To Dr Parry, for the best lot of two-tooth'd Rams, from the Spanish mixture, taking into the account the very superior quality of their wool, the premium of	10-10-0
1801	To T. Joyce esq for the finest piece of Navy Blue Broad Cloth from English Wool a premium of	10-10-0
	To J. Waldron esq. for the finest piece of white kerseymere from English wool, a premium of	5-5-0
	To Dr Parry, the Thanks of this society, accompanied by a honorary piece of plate, for his late excellent work entitled, "Facts and Observations tending to show the practicability and advantage of producing, in the British Isles, clothing wool equal to that of Spain".	10-10-0
	To Dr Parry, for a very superior Fleece of Wool, produced from a mixture of the Spanish and Ryeland breeds	5-5-0
1802	To Dr Parry, for the finest piece of Navy-Blue Broad – Cloth, also manufactured from Wool of his own Flock, a premium	5-5-0
1803	To Dr Parry, for the best lot of Sheep, the produce of a Spanish Ram with English Ewes, a premium of	5-5-0

1805	To Dr Parry, for the best piece of Navy-Blue Broad-Cloth from Lamb's Wool of British growth (ie Merino and British Ewes).	8-8-0
1807	To Messrs Yeates and Son, for manufacturing a piece of Navy-Blue Broad-Cloth, of Dr Parry's Merino Ryeland wool.	10-10-0
	To Thomas Joyce, a Piece of Uniform white Kerseymere from the wool of Dr Parry	5-5-0
1808	To Messrs, Yeats and Son, for manufacturing a piece of Navy-Blue Broad-Cloth, from Dr Parry's wool, a bounty of	8-8-0
	To Dr Parry, for exhibiting 10 rams of his flock at the Meeting in June and the fleeces of the same at the Annual Meeting	10-10-0
	To Dr Parry, for the best pen of Merino-Ryland ewes	10-10-0
	To Thomas Fowles, (Dr Parry's shepherd) for rearing the greatest number of Lambs in proportion to the number yeaned	3-3-0
1809	To Dr Parry, for exhibiting a Piece of Navy-Blue Broad-Cloth, made from the fleeces of Shearling Sheep, unshorn when Lambs, a premium of	8-8-0
1810	To Dr Parry, for the best lot of Breeding Ewes of the Anglo-Merino breed, a premium of	10-10-0
	To H. Hicks esq, for manufacturing the finest piece of Uniform White Kerseymere, a premium of	6-6-0
	To Dr Parry as Grower of the Wool	4-4-0
1813	Dr Parry exhibited 12 fleeces for inspection but not for premium	
1817	The Bedfordian Gold Medal	

Papers by Caleb Hillier Parry in Bath Society's Papers

Examination of two Parcels of English Rhubarb.
By W. Falconer MD FRS, Physician to the General Hospital and C.H. Parry MD, Physician to the Pauper Charity, Bath, Vol. IV, 1786, p. 405. Parry's papers p. 432, and p. 449.

An account of a Crop of Cabbages for which a Premium was awarded.
By Dr Parry. Bath, 4 December, 1798, Vol. IX, p. 343.

Two addresses to the Society, on the Subject of Improved Sheep by the Spanish mixture, their Wool and its Value in Superfine Cloth etc.
By C.H. Parry MD FRS, 12 November, 1804, Vol. X, p. 75.
10 December, 1804, Vol. X, p. 83.
Letter from Dr Parry, Circus, 24 November, 1806, Vol. XI, p. 164.

An Inquiry whether the pure Merino Breed of Sheep is now necessary in order to maintain the Growth of superfine wool in Great Britain.
By Dr Parry, Circus, 26 August, 1807, Vol. XI, p. 198.

Tables of the Female Descendants from 100 shearling Ewes during 20 years
By Dr Parry, Circus, 22 August, 1807, Vol. XI, p. 217.

An Inquiry into the Causes of the Decay of Wood, and the Means of preventing it.
By C.H. Parry, Circus, 30 September, 1807, Vol. XI, p. 226.

Correspondence relative of a very fertile Piece of Land at Wantage in Berkshire: with Remarks by Dr Parry. Vol. XI, p. 307.

Additional Observation on the Crossing of Animals.
By Dr Parry, 1807, Vol. XI, p. 314.

Syncope Anginosa

There appear to have been two editions or printings of this book, both published in 1799 (see p. 39). The copy in the Parry Library in the Bristol Medical Library appears to be the first. On the title page Parry is described as "Member of the College of Physicians of London and of the Royal Medical Society of Edinburgh". There is no dedication! In the copy in Bath in the Royal National Hospital for Rheumatic Diseases (the old General Hospital) Parry now has the additional description of "one of the physicians of the Bath General Hospital" (see below). Parry was appointed to the staff in 1799 presumably between the two printings. The later version includes the dedication.

AN

INQUIRY

INTO THE

SYMPTOMS AND CAUSES

OF THE

SYNCOPE ANGINOSA,

COMMONLY CALLED

ANGINA PECTORIS.

ILLUSTRATED BY DISSECTIONS.

BY

CALEB HILLIER PARRY, M.D.

MEMBER OF THE COLLEGE OF PHYSICIANS OF LONDON, AND OF THE ROYAL MEDICAL SOCIETY OF EDINBURGH.

BATH, PRINTED BY R. CRUTTWELL;
AND SOLD BY
CADELL AND DAVIES, STRAND, LONDON.

1799.

References

Chapter 1

1. Lewis, Sir Thomas. *Proceedings of the Cardiff Medical Society*, 1940–41, p. 71.
2. Murch, Jerom. *A History of the Presbyterian and General Baptist Churches in the West of England*, 1835.
3. Memorials of an Ancient Presbyterian Meeting House at Cirencester. *Transactions of the Unitarian Historical Society*, p. 273.
4. Defoe, Daniel. *A Tour through the whole Island of Great Britain*. Penguin Edition, p. 359.
5. Welsford, Jean. *Cirencester. A Historical Guide*, 1987.
6. Clifton-Taylor, A. *Cirencester; Another Six English Towns*, 1984.
7. Collier, Oswald. Two Cirencester families. Some notes on the families of Dix and Hillier. 1903. MSS in Gloucester Reference Library.
8. Collier, Oswald. op. cit.
9. Murch, Jerome. op. cit.
10. Parry, Sir Sydney. *The Quarterly Review*, 1897, Vol. 185, p. 94.
11. Murch, Jerome. op. cit.
12. Mocral, E.B. *Wilts and Gloucestershire Standard*, 13 June 1925 (Newspaper Article).
13. Mocral, E.B., op. cit.
14. Romans, Geoffrey H. The Story of Cirencester Grammar School 1958. *Gloucester Countryside*, Vol. 8, p. 252.
15. Fuller, E.A. Cirencester Free Grammar School 1886. *Trans. Bristol and Gloucestershire Archeological Society*, Vol. 9.
16. Parry, Charles H. in Macmichael (ed.) *Lives of British Physicians*, 1830.
17. Parry, Caleb H. *An Inquiry into the Sumptoms and Causes of Syncope Anginosa*, Bath 1799.
18. Parry, Caleb H. *Cases of Tetanus and Rabies Contagiosa*, Bath 1814.
19. Parry, Caleb H. MSS reminiscences dictated to his daughters (now in the Scott Polar Research Institute).
20. Rogers, D. (Area Librarian Warrington). Personal Communication.
21. Rogers, D. op. cit.
22. Turner, J. *Warrington Academy*, 1813–15 (reprinted 1957).
23. Rogers, D. op. cit.
24. Parry, Charles. op. cit.
25. McLachland, H. *Warrington Academy*, 1943.
26. McLachland. op. cit.
27. McLachland. op. cit.
28. Wells, Calvin. *Edward Rigby. A Medical Bulletin* (May & Baker) 1969, Vol. XV, 2 p. 39.

29. Batty-Shaw, A. *Norfolk and Norwich Hospital, Lives of the Medical Staff*, 1971, p. 23 (printed privately).
30. Denman, Thomas. *DNB*.
31. Parry, Sir Sydney. op. cit. p. 94.
32. Denman, Thomas. *An Essay on the Puerperal Fever*, 1785.
33. Gray, J. *History of the Royal Medical Society*, 1952.
34. Parry, Caleb Hillier. Presidential Address to the Medical Society, 1778.
35. Minutes of the University Meeting. 29 November 1777.
36. Minutes of the Medical Society. 11 April 1778.
37. Parry, Caleb H. op. cit. 1778
38. Minutes of the Medical Society. 1 June 1778.
39. Minutes of the Medical Society. 19 June 1778.
40. Gray, J. op. cit.
41. Parry, Calebus Hillier. *De Rabie Contagiosa*, 1778.
42. Cobbold, Mrs. Archivist, Ipswich. Personal Communication.
43. McLachland, H. op. cit.
44. Gray, J. op. cit.

Chapter 2

1. Warner, R. *The History of Bath*, 1801.
2. Hatton, J. *B.M.J.* 1925, Vol. 1, 1042.
3. Peach, R.E.M. *Street Lore of Bath*, 1893, London, p. 83.
4. Parry, Charles in Macmichael (ed.) *Lives of British Physicians*, 1830.
5. Baron, J. *The Life of Edward Jenner*, 1838, Vol. 1, p. 61.
6. Baron, J. op. cit. Vol. 1 p. 50.
7. *Science and Music in 18th Century Bath*, 1977, p. 83.
8. Parry, Caleb H. *An Essay on the Nature, Produce, Origin and Extension of the Merino Breed of Sheep*, 1807.
9. Parry, Caleb H. *Facts and Observations tending to show the practicability etc.*, 1800.
10. Parry, Sir Sydney. MSS Family History.
11. Hatton, J. **B.M.J.** 1925, Vol. I, 1042.
12. Eastes, H. *Bristol Med-Chi J.* Jan/Apr 1983, 18.
13. *Regulations and Transactions of the Gloucestershire Medical Society*, Royal College of Physicians, London.
14. Records of an old medical society. *B.M.J.* 1896, 1, 1296.
15. Cushing, H. *The Life of Sir William Osler*, Oxford, 1925. Letter dated 28 March 1915.
16. Parry, Caleb H. *An Inquiry into the Symptoms and Causes of Syncope Anginosa*, Bath 1799.
17. Parry, Caleb H. *Memoirs of the Medical Society of London*, 1792.3.77.
18. Parry, Caleb. *Phil. Trans. Royal Society*, 1811, 101.89.
19. Parry, Charles H. MSS Autobiography. (Bodleian).
20. Burke's Correspondence. Gen Ed. Thomas Copeland. Cambridge University Press Vol. 9.
21. Parry, Sir Sydney. *The Quarterly Review*, 1897, Vol. 185, p. 94.
22. Ison, W. *The Georgian Buildings of Bath*, 1980.
23. Baron, J. *Life of Jenner*, London, 1838, Vol. 1, p. 105/107.

24. Le Fanu, W.R. *A Bibibliography of Edward Jenner*, London 1951, Second edition ? 1985.
25. Parry, Sir Sydney. op. cit. MSS Family History.
26. Parry, Caleb H. *Bath Society's Papers*, 1798 Vol. IX p. 343.

Chapter 3

1. Warner, Richard. *History of Bath*, 1801.
2. *Bath Directory*, 1800.
3. Parry, Caleb. Collections from the unpublished Medical Writings, 1825, Vol. 2, p. 231.
4. Parry, Caleb. op. cit. p. 175.
5. Parry, Ann. *Parry of the Arctic*, 1963.
6. Archivist Royal Society. Personal Communication.
7. Reich, G.C. *On Fever and its Treatment*. Translated from the German by Charles Henry Parry. Bath 1801.
8. Parry, Charles, *Macmichael* (ed.) – *Lives of British Physicians*, 1830.
9. Austen, Jane. *Letters*, edited by R.W. Chapman, 1932.
10. Carlyon, Clement. *Early years and Late Reflections*, 1843.
11. Parry, Sir Sydney. Family History, MSS.
12. Sloman, Mrs S. Keeper of Art, Victoria Art Gallery Personal communication.
13. Audinet, Philip. *DNB*.
14. National Portrait Gallery, Personal Communication.
15. Sotheby's Personal Communication.
16. Parry, Miss A. Personal Communication.
17. Miller, G. *Letters of Edward Jenner etc.*, John Hopkins University Press 1983.
18. Miller, G. op. cit.
19. Miller, G. op. cit.
20. Letter, 6 July 1808, Sudeley Castle, Winchcombe, Glos.
21. Baron, J. *The Life of Edward Jenner* 1838 Vol. 2 p. 140.
22. Baron, J. op. cit. Vol. 2 p. 145.
23. Baron, J. op. cit. Vol. 2 p. 146.
24. Jenner letter. Wellcome M.S. 5240 (no 38).
25. Jenner letter. Wellcome M.S. 5235 (no 10).
26. Baron, J. op. cit. Vol. 2 p. 147.
27. Baron, J. op. cit. Vol. 2 p. 333.
28. Baron. op. cit. p. 365.
29. Miller, G. op. cit.
30. Saunders, Paul. *Edward Jenner, the Cheltenham Years*, 1982.
31. Parry, Caleb. *Bath Society's Papers*, 1807, Vol. XI, p. 226.
32. Ison W. *The Georgian Buildings of Bath*, 1980.
33. Cruickshank D. and Burton N. *Life in a Georgian City*, London 1990, p. 130.
34. Parry, Charles, *Macmichael (ed.) – Lives of British Physicians*, 1830.
35. Parry, Caleb. *Edinburgh Medical and Surgical Journal*, 1809, 5. 7.
36. Baron, J. *Life of Jenner*, 1838.
37. Parry – Banks letters. Transcribed by H.B. Carter, Bath Library.
38. Parry, Charles. op. cit.
39. Hatton, J. *B.M.J.* 1925, 1.1042.

40. Parry, Caleb. Collections from the unpublished Medical Writings of the late Caleb Hillier Parry. 1825. 2 Volumes.
41. Parry Caleb. op. cit. Vol. 2 p.17.
42. Parry Caleb. op. cit. Vol. 2 p. 31.
43. Parry Caleb. op. cit. Vol. 1 p. 252.
44. Parry Caleb. op. cit. Vol. 1 p. 181.
45. Parry, Caleb. cases of Tetanus and Rabies contagiosa. 1814.
46. Sakula, A. *J. Roy. Soc. Med.* 1990, 83, 788.
47. Britton, J. A *Topographical and historical description of the County of Wilts*, 1814.
48. Warner, Richard. op. cit.
49. Letter 24 March 1813. Jenner Museum, Berkeley.
50. Parry, Caleb. *Memoirs of the Medical Society of London*, 1792, III 77.
51. Parry, Caleb. *Elements of Pathology and Therapeutics*, 1815.
52. Parry, Caleb. *An Experimental Enquiry into the Nature of the Arterial Pulse etc.*, 1816.
53. Hunter, John. *Works*, 1835 edition, Vol. 3. p. 156.
54. Lewis, Sir T. *Proc. Cardiff Medical Society*, 1940/41, p. 71.
55. Parry, Caleb. *Medico Chir. Journal and Review*, 1816.
56. Parry, Charles. *Additional Experiments on the Arteries of Warm-blooded Animals*, London, 1819.
57. Warner. Rev. R. *Literary Recollections*, London, 1830.
58. Baron J. *Life of Jenner*, 1838, Vol. 2 p. 223.
59. Saunders, P. op. cit.

Chapter 4

1. Parry, Charles, Macmichael (ed.) in *Lives of British Physicians*, 1830.
2. Parry, Sir Sydney. MSS Notes.
3. Peach, R.E.M. *Street Lore of Bath*, 1893.
4. Parry, Caleb H. *An Essay on the Nature, Produce, Origin, and Extension of the Merino Breed of Sheep*, London, 1807.
5. Ison, Walter. *The Georgian Buildings of Bath*, 1980.
6. Parry, Sir Sydney. op. cit.
7. Parry, Caleb H. op. cit. Essay 1807.
8. Parry, Caleb H. *Facts and Observations tending to show the Practicability and Advantage etc.*, Bath, 1800.
9. Parry, Caleb H. *Bath Society's Papers*, 1807, XI, p. 198.
10. Parry, Caleb H. op. cit. Essay 1807.
11. Carter H.B. *His Majesty's Spanish Flock*, 1964.
12. Carter H.B. op. cit. 1964.
13. Parry, Charles op. cit.
14. Parry, Caleb H. op. cit. Facts and Observations 1800.
15. Practicus. *The Farmers' Journal*, 1802, June, p. 433.
16. Parry, Caleb H. *The Farmers' Journal*, 1802, July, p. 7.
17. Correspondence between Dr Caleb Hillier Parry FRS and Sir Joseph Banks PRS, 1800–1804. Transcript made by H.B. Carter from original documents, which are lodged in the Sutro Library at the University of San Francisco, California (Bath Ref Library).
18. Carter, H.B. op. cit.

19. Parry, Caleb H. *The Farmers Journal and Agricultural Advertiser*, No. 255, 17 August 1812, p. 369.
20. Parry, Caleb H. *The Farmers Journal and Agricultural Advertiser*, No 257, 31 August 1812, p. 385.
21. Parry, Caleb H. *The Farmers Journal and Agricultural Advertiser*,. No 260, 21 September 1812, p. 409.
22. Parry, Caleb H. *The Farmers Journal and Agricultural Advertiser*, No 262, 5 October 1812, p. 2.
23. Parry, Caleb H. *The Farmers Journal and Agricultural Advertiser*, No 265, 26 october 1812, p. 26.
24. Parry, Caleb H. *The Farmers Journal and Agricultural Advertiser*, No 266, 2 November 1812.
25. Parry, Caleb H. *The Farmers Journal and Agricultural Advertiser*, No 272, 14 December 1812, p. 81.
26. Parry, Caleb H. *Bath Society's Papers*, 1807, XI, p. 314.
27. Parry, Ann. *Parry of the Arctic*, 1963.
28. Herschel, W. *Philosophical Transactions*, 31 January 1782, p. 163 and 173.
29. Parry, Caleb H. Bath, July 29, 1809. Letter in the Scott Polar Research Institute.

Chapter 5

1. Parry, Charles. *Additional Experiments on the Arteries of Warm-blooded Animals*, London, 1819.
2. Parry, Charles. *A Memoir of the Revd. Joshua Parry*, Edited by Sir John E. Eardley-Wilmot, London 1872.
3. Bath and West Society. Minute Books.
4. Parry, Charles. MSS Autobiography.
5. Parry, Sir Sydney. *The Quarterly Review*, 1897, Vol. 185, p. 94–116.
6. Warner, Richard. *Literary Recollections*, London, 1830.
7. Baron. *Life of Jenner*, Vol. 2, London, 1838, p. 277.
8. *Gentleman's Magazine*, 1822, April, p. 372.
9. Lewis, Sir Thomas. *Proc. Cardiff Medical Society*, 1940–41, p. 85.

Chapter 6

1. Parry, Sir Sydney. MSS Family History.
2. Parry, Charles Henry. MSS Autobiography, Bodleian Library, Oxford.
3. Parry, Ann. *Parry of the Arctic*, London, 1963.
4. Parry, Sir Sydney. op. cit.
5. Parry, Sir Sydney. Letter to Bath Corporation, 14 February 1926.
6. Gahagan, Lucius. *Dictionary of British Sculptors*, Rupert Gunnis.
7. Monkland, G. *Supplement to the Literature and Literati of Bath*, 1855.
8. Parry, Sir Sydney. op. cit. Letter 1926.
9. Knight, Miss J. Keeper of Art, Victoria Art Gallery. Personal communication.
10. Vaughan, R. Temporary curator of the B.R.L.S.I. Museum. Personal Communication.
11. Parry, Charles Henry. op. cit.

12. Reich, G.C. *On Fever and its Treatment in General,* 1801.
13. Carlyon, C. *Early Years and Late Reflections,* 1843.
14. Coleridge, S.T. Letter to Sara Coleridge from Clausethal, 17 May 1799.
15. Parry, Charles Henry. op. cit.
16. Jenner, E. A letter to Charles Henry Parry MD FRS 1822.
17. Parry, Charles Henry. op. cit.
18. Rolls, R. *The Hospital of the Nation,* 1988.
19. Parry, Rev. Ed. *Memoirs of Rear Admiral Sir W Edward Parry,* 1857.
20. Parry, Rev. Ed. op. cit.
21. Parry, Ann. Personal Communication.
22. Parry, Ann. op. cit.

Chapter 7

1. Hudson, Kenneth, MA., F.S.A. *The Four Great Men of the Bath and West,* 1973.
2. Anon. *Bath Society's Papers,* 1780, Vol. 1 p. 185.
3. Falconer, William, M.D., F.R.S. *Bath Society's Papers,* 1780, Vol. 1 p. 220.
4. Rules and Orders of the Society. 1780 p. 51.
5. Falconer, W., M.D., F.R.S. *Bath Society's Papers,* 1786. Vol. 3. p. 405.
6. Farnell, W.B. *Bath Society's Papers,* 1786, Vol. 3. p. 414.
7. Falconer, W., M.D., F.R.S. *Bath Society's Papers,* 1786, Vol. 3. p. 422.
8. Parry, C.H., M.DS. *Bath Society's Papers,* 1786, Vol. 3. p. 431.
9. Parry, C.H., M.D. *Bath Society's Papers,* 1786, Vol. 3. p. 449.
10. Fothergill, A., M.D., F.R.S. *Bath Society's Papers,* 1786, Vol. 3. p. 453.
11. Fothergill, A., M.D., F.R.S. *Bath Society's Papers,* 1786, Vol. 3. p. 460.
12. Parry, Caleb, H. *Memoirs Medical Society of London,* 1792.3.77.
13. Parry, Caleb, H. *Elements of Pathology and Therapeutics,* 1815.
14. Parry, Caleb. op. cit. 3.77.
15. Parry, Caleb H. *Philosophical Trans. Roy. Soc.,* 1811, 101. 89.
16. Parry, Caleb H. *The Monthly Magazine,* May 1798, p. 348.
17. Parry, Caleb, H. op. cit. 3.77.
18. Kelly, E.C. *Encyclopaedia of Medical Sources,* Baltimore, 1948.
19. Lewis, Sir Thomas. *Proc. Cardiff Medical Society,* 1940/41, p. 71.
20. Parry, Caleb. *An Inquiry into the Symptoms and Causes of the Syncope Anginosa,* Bath, 1799.
21. Lewis, Sir Thomas. op. cit. 1940/41, p. 71.
22. Regulations and transactions of the Gloucestershire Medical Society. Royal College of Physicians. London.
23. Parry, Caleb Hillier. *An Inquiry into the Symptoms and Causes of the Syncope Anginosa, commonly called Angina Pectoris,* Bath, 1799.
24. Leibowitz, J.L. *The History of Coronary Heart Disease,* 1970.
25. Heberden, W. *Med. Trans. Coll. Phip.,* London, 1772, 11, 59.
26. Proudfit, W.L. *Br. Heart J.,* 1983, 50.209.
27. Rolleston, Sir Humphrey. *Anuals of Med. History,* 1925, VII. 205.
28. Parry, Caleb H. op. cit. 1799.
29. Osler, W., *Lectures on Angina and Allied States,* 1897.
30. Parry, Caleb H. op. cit. 1799.

31. Parry, Caleb H. op. cit. 1799.
32. Baron, John. *The Life of Edward Jenner M.D.*, 1838.
33. Parry, Caleb H. op. cit. 1799.
34. Fosbroke, John. *Supplement to – A Picturesque and Topographical Account of Cheltenham and its Vicinity*. By the Rev. T.D. Fosbroke, 1826, p. 271.
35. Parry, Caleb H. op. cit. 1799.
36. Lewis. Sir Thomas. *Proc. Cardiff Med. Soc.*, 1940/41, p. 71.
37. East, T. *The Story of Heart Disease*, 1956/57.
38. Lewis, Sir Thomas. op. cit. 1940/41, p. 71.
39. Rolleston, Sir Humphrey. op. cit. 1925, VII p. 205.
40. Bedford, Evan. *J Roy. Coll. Phip.*, London, 1968. 2. 127.
41. Proudfit, W.L. *Br. Heart J.*, 1981, 46.589.

Chapter 8

1. Bath Society. Rules, Orders and Premiums 1805. p. 54.
2. Parry C.H. An Inquiry into the Causes of the Decay of Wood, and the Means of Preventing it. *Bath Society's Papers*, 1807, Vol. XI, p. 226.
3. Parry, Caleb Hillier. *An Essay on the Nature, Produce, Origin and Extension of the Merino Breed of Sheep*, 1807.
4. Jackson, H. Patent Specification No 910. Preserving Timber. 1768.
5. *Encyclopaedia Brittanica*, 1797, Vol. 4, p. 457.
6. Rees's Cyclopaedia. 1819.
7. W.T. A short note signed W.T. *Bath Society Papers*, Vol. II, 1783, p. 114.
8. Haviland, James. *The improved practical measurer*, London, 1817, p. 499.
9. Skinner, H.A. *The Origin of Medical Terms*, Baltimore, 1949.
10. Parry, Caleb Hillier. *Collections from the unpublished Medical Writings of the late Caleb Hillier Parry*, London, 1825, Vol 1, 185.
11. Parry, Caleb Hillier. Observations on the Uitility of Venesection in Purpura. *Edinburgh Medical and Surgical Journal*, 1809, 5.7.
12. Parry, Caleb Hillier. *Collections etc.*, Vol. 1, 215.
13. Heberden, William. *Commentaries on the History and Cure of Diseases* (English translation), 1802, Chapter 78.
14. Schonlein, J.L. *Peliosis Rheumatic. In his Allegemeine und specielle Pathologie und Therapie*, 1837, 2, 48–49.
15. Henoch, E.H. *Ubeden Zusammenhang von Purpura und Intestinalstorungen*, Berl. klin. Wschr., 1868, 5, 517–19.
16. Hippocrates *Aphorisms*, Book V Loeb Classics.
17. Garrison, F.H. *Introduction to the History of medicine*, 1924.
18. Parry, C.H. *Collections from the unpublished Medical Writings*, 1825.

Note

The copy of this book in the Parry Library in Bristol was presented by the author to Mr George Norman, who for many years helped him with many post mortem dissections, and assisted in much of Parry's experimental work. He was the son of James Norman, who in 1786 had founded the Casualty Hospital in Kingsmead Square, to which Caleb Parry had been appointed physician.

19. Palmer, James F., 1835 edition of the *Works of John Hunter FRS Vol. III A Treatise on the Blood*, p. 216.

20. Hunter, J., 1835 edition of the *Works of John Hunter FRS Vol. III A Treatise on the Blood*, p. 156.
21. Palmer, James F. op. cit. p. 216.
22. Parry, Caleb H. *Elements of Pathology*, 1815, LVIII.
23. Parry, Caleb H. Letter to the Editor of the *Medico-Chirurgical Journal and Review*, 1816. Included in Charles Parry, *Additional Experiments on the Arteries*, 1819.
24. Lewis, Sir Thomas. *Proceedings of the Cardiff Medical Society*, 1940/41, p. 71.
25. Parry, Charles H. *Additional Experiments on the Arteries of Warm-Blooded Animals*, London, 1819.

Chapter 9

1. Parry, Charles. *Introductory Essays to the Collections from the unpublished medical writings of the late Caleb Hillier Parry*, 1825.
2. Review. *Lancet*, 1825, 7, 138–145.
3. Review. *Anderson's Quarterly Journal of Medicine and Surgery*, July 1825, Vol. II. pp. 318–25.
4. Review. op. cit. October 1825, Vol. II, pp. 477–96.
5. Review. *London Medical Repository*, 1825, Vol. III, pp. 401–16 and 476–86.
6. Parry, Charles. op. cit. 1825.
7. Parry, Charles. MSS Autobiography, Bodleian Library.
8. Parry, Charles in *McMichael's Lives of British Physicians*, p. 289.
9. Mainwaring R. *Anuals of Bath*, Bath, 1838, p. 234.
10. Parry, Caleb H. *Unpublished Medical Writings of the late*, 1825 Vol. I, p. 337, 1825.
11. Parry, Caleb H. op. cit. Vol. II, p. 111, 1825.
12. Parry, Caleb H. op. cit. Vol. II, p. 380, 1825.
13. Parry, Caleb H. op. cit. Vol. I, p. 478, 1825.
14. Parry, Caleb H. op. cit. Vol. II, p. 190, 1825.
15. Lewis, Sir Thomas. *Proc. Cardiff Medical Society*, 1940–41, p. 87.
16. Parry, Caleb H. op. cit. Vol. II, p. 29.
17. Parry, Caleb H. op. cit. Vol. I, p. 360.
18. Parry, Caleb H. op. cit. Vol. II, p. 457.

Chapter 10

1. Wright, R.W.M. *Bull. of the Victorian Art Gallery and Municipal Library*, Vol. 1, 1948, 225.
2. Kite, V.J. MSS in Bath Reference Library 1966.
3. Rolls, Roger. The Hospital of the Nation 1988. Personal communication.
4. Kite, V.J. op. cit.
5. Murch, J. *Biographical sketches of Bath Celebrities*, London, 1893.
6. Kite, V.J. op. cit.
7. Parry, Caleb H. *An Essay on the Nature, Produce, Origin and Extension of the Merino Breed of Sheep*, London, 1807.
8. Kite, V.J. op. cit.
9. Parry, Caleb H. *Cases of Tetanus and Rabies Contagiosa*, Bath, 1814.
10. LeFanu, W.R. *British peridocials of medicine*, Johns Hopkins, 1938.

11. Minutes of the United Hospital. No. 324. 29 September 1845.
12. Parry, Charles. MSS In Bodleian Library.
13. Monkland, G. *The Literature and Literate of Bath*, 1854.
14. Laurence, Godfrey. Personal communication (R.W. Falconer was physician to the General Hospital 1856–81).
15. Jones, Brian. MSS in Bristol University Medical Library.
16. Wright R.W.M. op. cit. Vol. 1, p. 225.
17. Wright R.W.M. op. cit. Vol. 1, p. 225.
18. Hatton, J. *B.M.J.* 1925, Vol. 1, 1042.
19. Parry, Sir Sydney. MSS Family history notes.
20. R.U.H. Managing Board. Minute 241, 18 October 1931.
21. R.U.H. Managing Board. Minute 242, 18 October 1931.
22. R.U.H. Managing Board. Minute 266, 14 December 1931.
23. Bath City Council. Minute, 7 June 1932, p. 405.
24. R.U.H. Managing Board. Minute 353, 13 June 1932.,
25. R.U.H. Managing Board. Minute 439, 19 December 1932.
26. Bevan, E. Mrs. Personal communication.
27. Wright R.W.M. op. cit. Vol. 1, p. 225.
28. R.U.H. Medical Board. Minute 3415, 27 April 1948.
29. R.U.H. Medical Board. Minute 3437, 28 May 1948.
30. R.U.H. Medical Board. Minute 3478, 22 July 1948.
31. Kindersley C.E. Report in *Bath Chronicle*, 28 July 1948.
32. Bath City Council. Minutes, 5 April 1949, p. 372.
33. Bath City Council. Minutes, 7 February 1950, p. 183.
34. Jones, Brian. op. cit. MSS.
35. Jones, Brian. op. cit. MSS

Notes

The Parry family possess a large volume of sketches and paintings mainly by Charles Parry's many daughters, including a few views of Summerhill and its gardens. They are mostly unsigned. They include an excellent coloured painting of the library. Charles Parry was a talented amateur artist. In 1797, for example, he won a silver medal in Bath for a drawing of a Madonna. In 1798, when he was studying medicine in London, he was also attending classes at the Royal Academy, and won a Gold Medal for a portrait of his sister Caroline. The painting of the library could be his work.

Papers about Parry

The following more recent publications have also been consulted:
Apley, J. 'Caleb Parry of Bath', *Medical Journal of the South West,* V71 (c) Jan. 1956.
Armitage, G. Parry's Disease. *University of Leeds Medical Journal*, 1956, 5, p. 9.
Bishop, T.H. *Caleb Hillier Parry*, The Medical Press, 1955, p. 401.
Blumer, G. Caleb Hillier Parry, *Connecticutt State Medical Journal*, 1954, p. 444.
Fitzwilliams, D.C.L. Caleb Hillier Parry, *Medical World*, 1946, p. 44.
Hoffenberg, R. The Thyroid and Osler. *J. of the Roy. Coll. of Physicians of London*, 1985, 19, p. 80.
Hudson, K. *History of the Bath and West*, 1976.
Jones, B. *Caleb Hillier Parry*, West of England Medical Society, 1991, 106, p. 101.
Murrell, T.G.C. 19th Century Masters of General Practice, *Medical Journal of Australia*, 1991.
Volpe, R. *Caleb Hillier Parry. The Endocriminologist*, 1994, 4, p. 15.

Index

Numbers in bold type indicate an illustration